# Biopolitics:
## Search for a More Human
## Political Science

**Also of Interest**

*Psychological Models in International Politics,* edited by Lawrence S. Falkowski

*Sociobiology: Beyond Nature/Nurture?,* edited by George W. Barlow and James Silverberg

# A Westview Special Study

## Biopolitics: Search for a More Human Political Science
## Thomas C. Wiegele

For the past decade, there has been an effort among many political scientists to incorporate biological information in the study of human behavior. This first comprehensive assessment of the rapidly emerging field of biopolitics examines current biologically oriented scholarship, covering the wide range from ethological evolutionary models of political life to psychophysiological components of elite political activity.

Dr. Wiegele thoroughly examines the theoretical underpinnings of a biopolitical perspective and asserts that, far from reducing the study of political behavior solely to biological processes, a biopolitical approach will encourage the development of a more comprehensive and human political science that takes into account the complex character of human nature. His concluding chapter explores a variety of curricular and research problems associated with future developments in biopolitics.

Thomas C. Wiegele is director of the Center for Biopolitical Research and associate professor in the department of political science at Northern Illinois University.

# Biopolitics:
## Search for a More Human Political Science
### Thomas C. Wiegele

Westview Press / Boulder, Colorado

*A Westview Special Study*

Copyright © 1979 by Westview Press, Inc.

Published in 1979 in the United States of America by
  Westview Press, Inc.
  5500 Central Avenue
  Boulder, Colorado 80301
  Frederick A. Praeger, Publisher


Library of Congress Cataloging in Publication Data
Wiegele, Thomas C.
  Biopolitics : search for a more human political science.
  (A Westview special study)
  1. Political science. 2. Biology. I. Title.
JA80.W53 320                    79-16252
ISBN 0-89158-691-1
ISBN 0-89158-751-9 pbk.


Printed and bound in the United States of America

*To Mary*

# Contents

# Table and Figures

# Acknowledgements

To produce a volume which crosses disciplines is, in many respects, a frightening task. This is the case because one is continuously confronted with the all too apparent limits to one's own knowledge. Clearly, this has been my experience. Nevertheless, I have had a good deal of encouragement from many quarters that served to provide a firm belief that this project was worth undertaking.

Three people stand out as having provided a broad faith in the value of pursuing biopolitical scholarship. Mr. Richard A. Ware, President of the Earhart Foundation, Dr. Jon D. Miller, Associate Dean for Research in the Graduate School at Northern Illinois University, and Dr. William R. Monat, President of Northern Illinois University have offered help and support at critical stages in the development of my own interest in biopolitics.

I am grateful also to those numerous scholars who have adopted a biological orientation in their political research. These individuals have been willing to sustain their work with the realization that they were moving into uncharted areas that could have turned out to be "professionally unproductive." Major commitments of time and energy were made by them to retrain themselves in order to discover what was "out there" in the life science disciplines.

Over the past few years I have had numerous profitable discussions with colleagues at Northern Illinois University regarding various aspects of biopolitics. These valued individuals include Professors Charles U. Larson and Richard Johanneson (both of the Department of Speech Communications), Professor Thomas McCanne (Department of Psychology), Professor Sharon A. Plowman (Department of Physical Education), Professor William M. Shearer (Department of Communication Disorders), Professor Manfred W. Wenner (Department of Political Science), and Professor Jerrold H. Zar (Department of Biological Sciences). Mr. Richard H. Cady, formerly at Northern Illinois University and presently Director of the Bureau of Institutional Research at the University of New Mexico, provided frequent lunch-time encounters that served the purpose of making me rethink an entire range of issues associated with measurement and methodology in biopolitical research.

A first draft of the manuscript was carefully read by Professor William E. Southern (Department of Biological Sciences, Northern Illinois University), Professor Glendon Schubert (Department of Political Science, University of Hawaii), Professor Albert Somit (Department of Political Science and Executive Vice President, State University of New York-Buffalo), Professor John C. Wahlke (Department of Political Science, University of Arizona), and Professor Meredith W. Watts (Department of Political Science, University of Wisconsin-Milwaukee). Their comments were most helpful.

I am appreciative of a sabbatical leave granted by the College of Liberal Arts and Sciences of Northern Illinois University that allowed me to launch the project and complete drafts of several initial chapters.

Two dedicated secretaries adopted what can only be referred to as a "personal interest" in typing successive drafts of the manuscript. Mrs. Margaret Casler and Mrs. Shelby Jarczyk provided careful and precise work at every stage in the process. Various administrative aspects of producing the manuscript were made much easier with the help of Ms. Joan M. Flaherty.

My wife Mary and our children, Joseph, Madelynn, Edward, Thomas, and Katharine, tolerated many emotional and intellectual "ups and downs" while the study was being written. I thank all of them for their kindness and patience.

The responsibility for any errors the study may contain is my own.

# Biopolitics:
## Search for a More Human Political Science

# 1
# Introduction

An effort has been underway within the field of political science, spanning a period from perhaps Albert Somit's 1968 seminal article to John Wahlke's 1978 presidential address to the American Political Science Association, to blend biological information into the study of human political behavior. Somit called for a more biologically-aware political science, while Wahlke exhorted the discipline to emerge from its prebehavioral posture. Between these calls for a biobehavioral sensitivity numerous papers and articles with just such an orientation have been produced. To date, because of the widely scattered publication outlets and conference and symposia presentations, the full impact and value of this work has gone largely unnoticed within the discipline.

This book argues that modern political scholarship could profit substantially from incorporating variables from the life sciences into the study of political phenomena. In a way, the volume represents an attempt to confront within the discipline what McManus et al. (1979:345) refer to as the "fallacy of arbitrary exclusion." They state that "this fallacy is committed whenever we, through ignorance or through adherence to a normative rule, exclude from consideration material efficiently present in the phenomenon being studied. This may be the result of strict adherence to rules of reduction or . . . the fallacy may be committed by defining a phenomenon in such a way that we artificially exclude similarities and connections with related phenomena." Although biologically oriented political scholarship has not been "arbitrarily excluded" from serious consideration by political scientists, it has suffered from a certain sense of isolation within the discipline. Many traditional political scientists generously consider biopolitics "interdisciplinary"—the less generous, would label it "extra-disciplinary." Regrettably, but quite understandably, much biopolitical work, because it borrows methodologies and terminologies from other disciplines completely foreign to the average political scientist, is dismissed as unintelligible, and therefore not very useful. And of course, as in every field of endeavor, there are those within the discipline whose vision and scope are so narrow that any expansion of knowledge is viewed as a "territorial" threat. Although I acknowledge that the introduction of biological information into the study of politics presents methodological and conceptual challenges, these challenges must be confronted if we aspire to precision and scientific credibility in our work.

The subtitle of this book—search for a more human political science—was chosen with some care.[1] I make no pretense of offering a definitive or even necessarily coherent body of knowledge; rather, to borrow a phrase from Mackenzie (1978), I have put together a "status report" on the continuing search for new information from the life sciences that can be used to further our understanding of the character of the human species. This book attempts to demonstrate that until now the search has been surprisingly fruitful, but that clearly it is incomplete and a far more intensive effort will be required in the years ahead.

Initially, the organization of the book presented substantial difficulties. Scholars working in biopolitics have tended to group themselves in ways not always acceptable to the current mind-set of those in the discipline of political science. Likewise, scholars from the life sciences might have preferred an organizational format more in keeping with their thinking, with chapters structured around topics such as ethology, psychophysiology, medicine, biochemistry, neuroanatomy, and psychopharmacology. However, I chose to organize the volume in chapter catergories that would be clearly familiar to the practicing political scientist: the political system, political elites, international relations, and political conflict. In addition, the opening theoretical chapter discusses the interest of biopolitical scientists in a fundamental reordering of the discipline.

This organizational decision had corresponding substantive consequences. Rather than projecting biopolitics as a subfield in its own right—which it may ultimately become—it has been presented as a potentially intimate part of every subfield in the discipline. Indeed, the relationship between the life sciences and political science is so symbiotic that to ignore it, one must awkwardly step around the questions it presents, carefully avoiding the issues and challenges of the relationship.

It is important to underscore that the book deals almost exclusively with scholarship produced by political scientists. Again, this was a conscious decision with several implications. The natural science literature that undergirds biopolitical work might appropriately have been included—much of it, though written for other audiences, provides a great deal of politically relevant information. But that literature is so voluminous that the resulting study would have been unwieldy and might have obscured the political research that is our prime focus. This, then, is a book that asks readers to probe more deeply into a particular line of inquiry by going directly to the works cited and by examining the biological literature underlying that work. Such investigation is sure to be rewarding, since most political scientists are careful to spell out the linkages between their scholarship and that of relevant life scientists. The biological work cited suggests a good foundation for further immersion in each topic. Having limited the book's scope to political research with biological implications, I also decided not to include an extended review of the standard political literature in any subfield; that work is readily available and familiar to most readers.

Although a biopolitical orientation has been in evidence within political science for at least ten years, development within that period has been uneven. As might be expected, the first works were highly speculative, pointing out possible relationships between biology and politics. These writings were followed by more carefully circumscribed empirical studies. Quite understandably, political philosophers and specialists in empirical political behavior have made the greatest quantitative contribution to biopolitical scholarship. Students of international relations, comparative politics, and human conflict, for example, have been slower to produce scholarship with a biopolitical orientation; hence the volume of work in these areas is a bit thin. As more work is completed, these imbalances will be corrected.

It will be obvious to readers of this volume that two broad divisions exist within the biopolitical community. One might be described loosely as "evolutionary," drawing on the literature of ethology and sociobiology. The other can be summed up under the catch-all heading of "physiology." Physiologically oriented researchers have utilized work dealing with medicine, psychophysiology, psychopharmacology, nutrition, public health, etc. Another distinction appears as we examine past biopolitical research: those scholars with an evolutionary thrust seem to have dealt primarily with mass issues that in some way affect all of mankind, while scholars with a physiological thrust have dealt primarily with small groups or individual human beings. However, as the body of literature in biopolitics grows, this distinction is becoming increasingly blurred. As we shall see, research methods from ethology can be used just as comfortably to study either small groups or individuals. Moreover, physiological data can be collected for large populations. A careful bibliographic analysis of past biopolitical research can be found in Somit et al. (1978).

While the charge of biological reductionism has frequently been levelled against scholars who advocate a biopolitical perspective, the charge has no basis in fact. Biopolitical writers have been necessarily sensitive to the interrelationships of the rich variety of factors that affect political behavior. The biopolitical perspective put forward in this volume is anything but reductionist; in fact, it encourages the development of a far more comprehensive political science—a discipline willing and eager to confront and, where appropriate, incorporate information from the life sciences. Indeed, it might be argued that the reductionist label could be applied more appropriately to present-day "traditional" political science, which too often reduces the explanation of political behavior to exclusively rationalist considerations.

As knowledge within the life sciences has burgeoned, its impact has been acknowledged by scholars in other disciplines. Writers in economics (Hirshleifer, 1977), sociology (van den Berghe, 1974), and psychology (Campbell, 1975) have produced strong theoretical papers linking biological information with their respective fields. Bioanthropology has been a recognized subfield for quite some time. In sociology advocates of biological approaches have sparked brisk controversies that have been in evidence at conventions and in the central journals for at least the past four years.[2] Considered in toto, the influence of the life sciences on the social sciences has been reasonably significant so far. Within each discipline there is a sensitive and articulate awareness of the challenging potential of a biological perspective. However, with the possible exception of bioanthropology, the social sciences have had difficulty in completely accepting biologically oriented scholarship. Perhaps this volume can contribute to an anchoring within political science.

## Notes

1. The psychological dimension of political life has been broadly explored in Knutson (1972).

2. Caplan (1978) documents the extent of such controversy across several disciplines.

## References

Campbell, D. T. (1975) "On the Conflicts between Biological and Social Evolution and between Psychology and Moral Tradition." *American Psychologist*, December:1103-1126.

Caplan, S. L., ed. (1978) *The Sociobiology Debate: Readings on Ethical and Scientific Issues.* New York: Harper and Row.

Hirshleifer, J. (1977) "Economics from a Biological Point of View."
    *Journal of Law and Economics* 20, 1, April:1-52.
Knutson, J. N. (1972) *The Human Basis of the Polity: A Psycho-
    logical Study of Political Men.* Chicago: Aldine-Atherton.
Mackenzie, W. (1978) *Biological Ideas In Politics.* New York: Pen-
    guin Books.
McManus, J., C. D. Laughlin, Jr. and E. G. d'Aquili. (1979) "Con-
    cepts, Methods, and Conclusions," in E. G. d'Aquili,
    C. D. Laughlin and J. McManus, eds., *The Spectrum of
    Ritual: A Biogenetic Structural Analysis.* New York: Col-
    umbia University Press.
Somit, A., S. A. Peterson and W. D. Richardson. (1978) *The Literature
    of Biopolitics, 1963-1977.* DeKalb, Illinois: Center for
    Biopolitical Research.
van den Berghe, P. L. (1974) "Bringing Beasts Back In: Toward a Bio-
    social Theory of Aggression." *American Sociological Re-
    view* 39, December:777-788.

# 2
# Theoretical Foundations
# of Biopolitics

Since World War II political science has undergone a behavioral revolution that has attempted to make the discipline more scientific. Putting "science" into political science has usually meant employing scientific methods to study human behavior. The emphasis on more precise methods, more rigorously designed research projects, and more carefully generated findings has vastly expanded our knowledge about political behavior. However, a biopolitical approach suggests something quite beyond this. Biopolitics asks political scientists to use the methods of scientific inquiry and to include in their examinations the substantive findings of the human life sciences. Indeed, the advances of twentieth-century biology and other life sciences represent a challenge to political science that can no longer be ignored.

This challenge is as old as antiquity. In ancient Greece a man was judged by his physical strength, his courage, his power, and his intellect. The wise person developed the faculties of body, soul, and mind. Socrates, as described by Plato, is quoted as remarking, "I would say some God has given two arts to mankind, music and gymnastics, . . . not for soul or body particularly. . . but for both together, in order that they may be fitted together in concord, by being strained and slackened to the proper point." In the *Protagoras* Plato reflects on the need for balance in the human person saying that "the life of man in every part has need of harmony and rhythm." In the eighth chapter of the *Laws of Athenian States* Plato argued that "the

7

aim of right education is to bring out the best conditions of body and mind." Moreover, when Plato relates that man is a political animal he recognizes that the person is a behaving, social creature who has a physical, biological constitution. Indeed, the two are one; and for us to accurately probe the human person we must understand the union of both the biological as well as the cognitive and psychological.

The term "biology" as used in this volume refers to "the science of living matter in all its forms and phenomena" *(Webster's New Century Dictionary,* 1956). Obviously this broad definition encompasses many subspecialties in the study of a human organism; as the need arises, these subspecialties will be carefully distinguished from the more general life science usage.

Biopolitics is an orientation to political inquiry that acknowledges the person as a complex rational, emotional, biological creature. Although biopolitics has attempted to blend strands of knowledge from both the life sciences and the social sciences in an effort to better understand human political behavior, it does not attempt to reduce all political behavior to simply a discussion of biological aspects. Instead, biopolitical research has tried to demonstrate that many human activities, formerly believed to be exclusively rational or psychological in character, are frequently influenced and tempered by biological factors.

In acknowledging the impact of biological variables on political behavior, the political scientist is not in any way denying that people have intellects with rational powers of reasoning. Rather, it might be argued that political science has often been antihumanistic because it has not adequately taken into account the biological aspects of political behavior. By looking at the entire person as a biological as well as an intellectual and emotional creature, we are assuming a much more humanistic approach. Biopolitics, then, can be viewed as an effort to restore humanism to political inquiry.

Biopolitics also does not attempt to oversimplify the impact of biological variables by saying that human political behavior is biologically determined. Although biology does set limits on human activity and necessarily influences human behavior, it is not an exclusive determinant of that behavior. Rational activity and psychological considerations are major factors; and social processes and culture also frequently mediate between the individual's nature and political behavior.

Moreover, biopolitics is not the exclusive preserve of a single academic discipline. The division of labor within most universities today is apportioned along traditional disciplinary lines, such as a department of physics, a department of history, a department of political science, a department of biology, a department of economics, and so on. These divisions are appropriate and facilitate administrative matters within the university context, but they do not necessarily accurately delineate the variety of approaches to the study of human activity. It might be more useful to organize a department of human behavior, which does not now exist in most universities and include in it a variety of specialists—an economist, a political scientist, a biologist, a chemist, and so on.

A number of researchers have been working in the area of biology and politics during the past few years. Reviewing the work of these researchers—looking at the position that each has taken and pointing out the deficiencies that each has seen in political science—should yield a better understanding of the importance of incorporating biological perspectives into the study of political behavior.

## Different Approaches to Biopolitics

The emerging area of biopolitics represents a challenge to the established interests of political scientists, for it says, in effect, that "something" has been missing from the study of human political behavior; that previous work has been incomplete. The first writer known to utilize the term "biopolitics" was Morley Roberts, who in 1938 published *Bio-Politics: An Essay in Physiology, Pathology, and Politics of the Social and Somatic Organism*. Though it anticipated numerous associations between biological phenomena and human political behavior, the book was essentially speculative and analogical. Since the 1960s, biopolitically oriented scholars have been adding to the discipline on more empirical grounds. In their distinctive but compatible approaches to biopolitics, these writers have created an awareness of the impact of life sciences on the traditional study of politics.

## Lynton Caldwell

Perhaps the first contemporary political scientist to document the growing impact of biological information on the analysis of political phenomena and policy, Caldwell (1964) was sensitive to the entire range of concerns that were ultimately included in the present area of biopolitics. His essay of fifteen years ago described some of the shortcomings of the discipline: "political science in America has, in its subconscious, assumed the infinite perfectibility of man" (Caldwell, 1964:2). This observation suggested that political scientists had not taken into account the biological limits imposed on the human species by evolution. Such limits restrict the "malleability range" and the concept of tabula rasa that so attracted the ancients. Moreover, "an explosion of biological knowledge and technology is raising questions of public policy which until recently were hypothetic" (Caldwell, 1964:2). Nevertheless, Caldwell argued that society frequently had remained insensitive to the import of biological advances until those advances began to have serious effects upon the social order. As an example, he pointed out that the improvement of public health contributed to the explosion of population during the twentieth century, a development governments have reacted slowly to, if at all.

For Caldwell the study of biopolitics is focused essentially in the arena of public policy. (See also Caldwell and DeVille, 1976.) He developed two broad groupings of biopolitical policy issues. The first he termed "environmental issues," which result when human choice either deliberately or inadvertently alters the environment in ways that despoil the natural habitat. The infusion of radioactive debris, the widespread use of chemical pesticides, and the effects of noise and crowding on human beings are perhaps the clearest examples. The second category

of issues is more personal. Termed "specifically physiological," they result from "the use of cigarettes, tranquilizers,
narcotics, and alcohol—and extending to the biochemical
control of personality" (Caldwell, 1964:6). This group also
includes questions of human reproduction and biological
warfare.

In spite of the second category, for Caldwell biopolitics must
relate essentially to issues of public policy that have a
biological basis. He argues that

> [t]he coincident and related explosions of human population
> and of biological knowledge may conceivably represent the
> most critical stage in human evolution since the last great ice
> age. The ability and necessity to control the numbers and hence
> (in some respects) the genetic characteristics of future popula-
> tions could create a situation without precedent in human exis-
> tence. And, in addition, the availability and refinement of chemo-
> psychiatric drugs suggest both hoped-for and frightening pos-
> sibilities for the manipulation and control of human behavior.
> Never before have the necessity and the possibility of control
> over man occurred at so decisive a conjunction (Caldwell,
> 1964:8).

To carry these views a bit further, Caldwell (1964:11-12)
lamented that "we have not yet laid down a comprehensive
biological foundation upon which a 'science of mankind' can
safely be erected." Reflecting his interest in a public policy
orientation, Caldwell looked forward to the development of a
scientifically sound biopolicy for political society. "Without
the interrelation and distillation of scientific findings into
issues amenable to political action, the gap between science
and politics cannot be successfully bridged" (Caldwell,
1964:15). Though he recognized many of the emerging
biologically related issues of political behavior, Caldwell's
major concern was the rapidly escalating infusion of biological
information into questions of public policy. He argued with
foresight that the study of biopolitics will demand "an
extraordinary fusion of understanding, audacity, and humil-
ity" (1964:16).

## Albert Somit

Caldwell emphasized public policy, but Somit (1968) was probably the first American political scientist to point out that new developments in the life sciences, especially in ethology and psychopharmacology, could influence the kind of judgments political scientists make about political behavior. "The biological sciences," wrote Somit (1968:550) "have much to teach political scientists. Recent findings increasingly suggest that there is a physiological or biological element operating in a good deal of what we call 'social' or 'political' behavior." Moreover, he indicated that a biological approach might very well allow us "to account for political phenomena for which we as yet have no satisfactory explanation" (1968:550).

Somit singled out two disciplines that he felt would have a strong impact upon political science: ethology, the study of animal social behavior in evolutionary perspective, and psychopharmacology, the study of drugs or substances that effect the human mind. While most political scientists view "the proper study of mankind as man" and would tend to reject knowledge developed from the study of animals, Somit (1968:551) pointed out that in their study of the evolutionary changes in animals, ethologists have discovered that "natural selection has worked to fashion, for each species, behavior patterns which identify that species almost as readily as do its physical characteristics." Ethological scholarship suggests that humanity too has an evolutionary history, and that conceivably the human species exhibits behavior patterns that are biologically transmitted and serve to categorize human social activity.

One advantage of working with animals is that the researcher has a greater freedom to engage in experimentation and direct observation. Hypotheses dealing with dominance and submission, territoriality, courtship, mating, relations with other members of the species, care of infants, and the like can be widely explored in test situations. Such experimentation is normally not done with human subjects for a variety of moral and ethical reasons, so we must rely on work with animals to provide knowledge that can lead to new insights about human social behavior.

Psychopharmacology, however, is a different matter. Somit indicates that during the 1950s, discoveries that some drugs were helpful in treating long-unfathomable mental and emotional illnesses led to a virtual revolution in therapeutic practices for patients in mental institutions. This discussion does not include drug abuse by nonprofessionals, which has ruined many lives over the past decade. Drugs have been found, for example, that improve memory, facilitate intellectual performance, and change established behavior patterns.

The reader might well ask why Somit has singled out ethology and psychopharmacology—widely diverging disciplines—to make his case for a biological perspective in political science. The answer is of some theoretical interest. If psychoactive drugs can influence human behavior, and it certainly appears that they can, "it follows that they do so by modifying . . . the physiological and bio-chemical functioning of the human organism. These changes produce, in turn, . . . changes in the behavior of the 'mind.' This is to say no more or no less than that there is a biological basis for a good deal of what we have hitherto insisted on treating as purely 'psychic' or 'mental' phemomena" (Somit, 1968:560). The study of drugs appears to have confirmed that there is a "direct link between biology and behavior in man as well as in other forms of life."

What does this connection between the biological and the behavioral mean for political science? Although we cannot make accurate predictions, some implications appear on the horizon. For example, the study of political behavior will necessarily become more complex. Up to the present political scientists have looked upon political beliefs and behaviors as "essentially psychic phenomena," that is, the result of learning and social conditioning. In the future, human genetic inheritance will have to be taken into account along with present-day biological factors. This will make our research projects much more complicated, but more accurate.

In political philosophy, we have a continuing interest in

individuals and their relationship to the repository of political power, the state. Will a deeper understanding of human nature alter the relationships between individuals and the state? If certain forms of criminality are shown to have a genetic basis, "we will have to reconsider our notions of guilt, of punishment, and of the manner whereby we can best reform the chronic lawbreaker" (Somit, 1968:563). Indeed the very basis of the political process could be dramatically changed by a political struggle concerning who should exercise power over the technology of biological control. Somit warned that drug technologies could be used indiscriminately by governments, with public sanction, against certain groups, such as prisoners of war or indigenous populations in captured countries.

## Peter Corning

"In what must surely rank as one of the strangest episodes in the entire history of science," observed Corning (1971:321), "two generations of our immediate forebearers in the social sciences managed virtually to ignore the 'Darwinian' theory of biological evolution and to exclude from their purview any sustained consideration of the role of biological factors in the shaping of human behavior." With this comment as background, Corning has developed an evolutionary-adaptive perspective on the political system and on certain general aspects of human behavior. He argues that "without an understanding of the evolutionary origins in the genetic basis of behavior, we cannot hope to grasp the inner principles by which human life is organized; a full explanation of human behavior must include not only biological variables but, equally important, an understanding of the evolutionary functions and survival consequences of behavior" (1971:321). Corning's general criticism of contemporary political science is that "our immediate heritage in the social sciences has been one of environmental (cultural) determinism and a functionalism without a theory—that is, a functionalism that somehow became disconnected from the only scientifically acceptable explanation of the origin, nature, and 'purpose' of human life." As a result of this outlook, in which the environment more or less determined political life, political scientists were viewing people as creatures more akin to essences than to real human beings—human beings who have bodies and emotions, who cry, and who suffer pain. Indeed, said Corning (1971:323), quoting Ashley Montague disapprovingly, "Man is man because he has no instincts, because everything he is and everything he has become he has learned, acquired, from his culture, from the man made part of his environment, from other human beings." Corning suggests that much of political science implicitly views people as little more than stimulus-response (s-r) models that can be manipulated by changes in the environment. Little attention is given to the fact that an individual human being is a unique creature who processes inputs for the environment in unique ways and reaches conclusions about the environment that may or may not accord with the general judgments of others.

With his criticism that "there has been no systematic attempt to incorporate into the thinking of the discipline [of political science] the perspective of modern evolutionary biology and current knowledge about biological components of behavior," Corning (1971:325) presents what he calls an evolutionary model of society. "Evolution is a process through which a population of organisms enhances its survival potential by successive genetic changes, or adaptations. Random mutations, genetic recombinations (or reshuffling), and behavioral variation provide the raw material for adaptation. This raw material is then tested in the environment for its survival value, or relative fitness, and the 'editing' process is called natural selection" (1971: 326-327). He emphasizes "that the basic survival unit is not the isolated individual, as it is commonly supposed, but rather the gene pool, or breeding population" (1971:327).

All of this is a preface to Corning's major point, which is that political life, a form of group life, "is essentially a biological phenomenon with specific survival value. . . . Whatever else may be involved in the social behavior of human beings, it is clear that altruism, cooperation, and group loyalty also have genetic support; genes that make for group-serving behavior, along with genes for self-serving behavior, would have been favored by natural selection" (1971:327-328). The term "fitness," as used by biological writers, is roughly equivalent to the phrase "general welfare" as used by political scientists. Echoing some of the comments by Somit, Corning (1971:330) argues, "behaviors that contribute to reproduction success will be favored by natural selection, and the genetic basis for those successful behaviors will be incorporated into a population gene pool." Therefore, according to Corning's line of argument, "there is . . . a feedback process at work between behavior and its biological base."

What does this evolutionary orientation add up to with regard to our perception of human political behavior? Corning's response is that the species can be incorporated into a biological and evolutionary framework, which then can be utilized to look at human political behavior. Indeed, says Corning (1971:339), "the basic structure of every human society, including our own, is 'determined' in a general way by a number of ongoing and species-specific *biological needs* (subject to some individual and geographical variation) that must be continually satisfied if the species, and the individuals who compose it, are to survive in the long run." We are all familiar with the basic needs first suggested by Maslow (1943, 1954) and introduced into political science by James Davies (1963) in his book *Human Nature in Politics*. They include nutrients, good health, shelter, clothing, security, and so on. Corning accuses political scientists of taking these needs for granted. Indeed, he points out that "the meeting of our species-preserving biological needs is a continuing enterprise, and the great preponderance, by far, of human activity the world over is devoted to various aspects of it" (Corning, 1971:340).

Let us pause briefly to review Corning's argument. He states that human beings are biological creatures living in interrelated environments on this planet. They interact with that environment in order to satisfy their basic needs. The way they interact has shaped the way they behave. The more adaptive human behaviors are, the better people interact with the environment, and therefore the better situation they create for themselves in terms of survival. Indeed, Corning set forth a conceptualization of human biological makeup as the necessary linkage between environmental stimuli and behavioral responses. This should not be interpreted as a simple social Darwinism or an environmental kind of determinism, because any given individual has a unique biological constitution though many biological traits are shared with others in the same human population.

What is the implication of Corning's approach to the study of political science? In an evolutionary sense, Corning (1971:367) defines the political system as "a functional division of labor within the collective survival enterprise. . . . Political systems are accumulations of evolved cultural responses to the problems of survival in specific natural and cultural environments." Thus, politics becomes "not equivalent to the struggle for power." Nor is it "equivalent to the role of refereeing the fights between the contending interest groups." Nor is it "merely a matter of vying for governmental benefits on the part of this or that interest." Instead, politics "fits the evolutionary conception of society as a goal directed enterprise in which the 'authoritative allocation of values,' in Easton's terminology, must have as its object James Madison's 'permanent aggregate interests of the community'" (Easton, 1965:29 quoted in Corning, 1971:367). Corning proposed that the evolutionary perspective be utilized as a general theory of human behavior, including, of course, political behavior. He observed that many of the contemporary approaches to social and political analysis, such as systems analysis and decision-making theory, could also be well suited to operationalizing an evolutionary outlook within political science.

In the operationalizing process we must look at society in evolutionary terms. Once that is done, says Corning (1976), we can proceed to analyze specific social behaviors, including institutions and values, in the light of their consequences for the survival or environmental fitness of society. "The basic question for the social scientist is: how does a particular social phenomenon help (or hinder) the human animal and satisfy his survival needs? And how does it affect the survival and reproduction efficacy of his society as a collectivity?'' If we use this framework of inquiry, it is possible for us to apply it to every aspect of political life. For example, we can ask, how does the government of the state of Illinois contribute to the survival requirements of its citizens. Or, how does the federal government contribute to or detract from the survival needs of the American society? Of course Corning is not oblivious to the further question of values: what ought to be the survival strategies of a particular society given the evolutionary framework of analysis? This last question raises yet another important issue: how does one recast the discipline of political science into a survival orientation?

This question was answered by Corning (1976) in an extensive later work that advanced what he referred to as a biologically oriented policy science. This, he said, should be organized around a survivalist ethic, which could become the foundation for a stewardship model of social ethics or of social practice. The stewardship model would be "concerned with maximizing the long term survival chances of the human species as a corporate entity" (Corning, 1976:137). The difficulty with this model is that analysts need some way of answering questions regarding the nature of survivability, how well a society or a system fares in terms of survival, what kinds of chances it might have in the future, and how it is adjusting to perceived future demands. In order to handle such a range of questions, one must first develop a system of survival indicators; second, one must have some way of forecasting once a survivalist mode has been adopted; and third, one needs to develop systems analyses that will assess the consequences of various survival-related decisions for a given political system.

Corning conceives of a survival indicator as roughly analogous to a social indicator that provides an analyst with data about behavior or a social system under study. The major difference is that survival indicators focus primarily on very basic types of issues. For example, he argues (1976:144) that "the objective is to try to measure as rigorously as possible the basic survival and reproductive needs of a human population; we are interested in establishing criteria and measuring rods for determining whether or not the basic survival minima are being satisfied." Corning's present work focuses on eleven basic survival needs: food, water, energy, basic raw materials, shelter, technology, environmental quality, health, physical security, factors influencing reproduction, and certain postulated social/psychological needs. Data is being collected for each one of these needs and assessments will be made as to how well a given political unit fulfills those needs. Corning is quick to point out that in order for political policymakers to engage in survival-oriented decision making they need to develop certain minimal requirements for survival, just as health researchers have determined minimal nutritional requirements. He argues that it is not beyond the realm of human capabilities to develop such basic survival criteria.

Given the rapid depletion of resources within our environment and the continuing necessity to utilize those resources, Corning insists that a survival-oriented political science will need to develop forecasting tools capable of accurately projecting needs for the future. These future needs will form the bases for nationally determined planning efforts. It will be an important and difficult task to develop a set of value preferences for those needs and to project those value preferences into the future as well.

Finally, Corning suggests that political scientists should become heavily involved in rigorous systems analyses for the purpose of developing some method of assessing the general welfare. Indeed, he calls for what he refers to as "welfare impact analyses." Such analyses would explore how well or to what end various decisions affect the political system in a survival context. Systems analysts would also look at long term trends in an attempt to determine whether those trends were producing an adverse or beneficial effect on the general welfare. Corning contends that a high political priority should be a reevaluation of the requirements for the general welfare. He insists that "the human species is in serious trouble, and powerful forces are corroding whatever measure of the 'good life' we may have achieved in some areas of the globe" (1976:151). Thus, "man is threatened by his very success and is

locked into unstable and dangerous modes of adaptation." If
we do not begin to examine our chances for survival seriously
and immediately, we will ultimately enter the future without a
clear idea of where we want to go or how we want to get there.

Corning has posited an open-ended adaptive approach to the
study of the polity in which human beings might be able to
guide their own evolutionary destinies to achieve a more likely
chance of survival. There are, of course, some difficulties
associated with his conceptualizations: Does the international
system adopt a survivalist orientation to politics on an
international level, on a system-wide level, on a national level,
or on all levels simultaneously? What if some nations have an
advantage in the struggle for power in the international system
over those who are reassessing the general welfare? Who shall
be responsible for beginning the process of reorienting
governments toward a survival-oriented policy science? These
questions are raised to point out that in order for this planet to
adopt a survival-oriented approach there are numerous
roadblocks that will have to be removed first, and it seems that
the removal of those roadblocks might occupy a good deal of
our initiative in the near future. However, it is quite likely that
the relatively recent energy crisis and the problems associated
with it could help alert everyone to the need for a survival-oriented political science.

## Glendon Schubert

For some years Schubert has been intimately engaged in
rethinking the basic structure and research paradigms of
political science; his writings have had a powerful impact on
biopolitical scholars. These innovating efforts have had both a
micropolitical sensitivity and a macropolitical sweep.

Expressing a concern with the shallowness of our knowledge
about political behavior, Schubert has written:

> A major limitation of political behavioral research is that it is
> premised on a paradigm of human behavior that is only skin-
> deep—because the observations never attempt to get inside the
> soma [body] except inferentially. Even what is known of

cognition is based upon externally observed—or at least, auditioned—behavior. What is always and everywhere most important to all human beings is what is going on *inside* of themselves at any particular moment. . . [B]ut what political behavioralism begins and rests its case with is what can be perceived to have occurred in some monitorable and measurable way *outside* of persons. Our task is to get beyond interactions and into transactions; and the only way to do that is by invoking theories, methods, and skills that permit us to include biological variables in our regression equations. Environment must be seen as a set of variables, not as the sole primal cause of all behavior; the history of politics should begin before our species can be differentiated as such; and our political behavior studies must contribute to, and become reconciled with, a theory of animal behavior that includes life forms whose morphological appearance is strikingly unanthropomorphic (1975:417).

The reader should not interpret that last sentence to mean that Schubert has reduced political science to the study of animal behavior. What concerns him (1976:161) is that "political scientists thus far have seemed somehow able to ignore the lesson learned by zoologists and physiological psychologists, who went through all this [research on motivation] (with . . . animals, which could not talk but nevertheless seemed to be motivated) half a century ago." In these two fields, says Schubert (1976:161), scientists "now concede the critical importance of checking their field (or zoo) observations with neurological and endocrinological laboratory findings concerning the biophysics and biochemistry of animal motivational systems." The disciplines that will—and should—have a critical impact on political science are microbiology, biochemistry, biophysics, molecular biology, genetics and genetic engineering, and neurophysiology.

To Schubert, the adoption of a biopolitical approach represents a major challenge to the traditional folk wisdom of political science. His insights are worth quoting at length:

Biological theory implies the rejection of the presumption that our political theory as a species began 2,500 years ago in Athens

or (alternatively) as described in "naturalistic" fables (whether
optimistic like that of Rousseau or pessimistic like that of
Hobbes). . . . The roots of political behavior go back not
thousands but millions of years; and political man did not
spring . . . from the forehead of Socrates—as our teaching of the
wellsprings of political philosophy might lead innocents to
infer. The implications of contemporary research in physical
anthropology, archeology, paleontology, and related sciences
are going to jack political philosophy off its classical
assumptions—once political scientists become better educated
in, and start facing up to the facts of biological life including
their own life history as a species (Schubert, 1976:164-165).

In that paragraph just quoted Schubert advances a powerful
argument: political behavior has traditionally been explained
as having its beginnings in the ancient wisdom of classical
Greece over 2,000 years ago. He is concerned that such a *narrow*
time span will distort our views about political life, and
encourages political scientists to adopt a much broader time
frame—one that will take political scholarship back a million
or more years. Such a perspective will necessarily require
political scientists to examine the work of anthropologists and
others who know a great deal about the origins of human social
and political activity. By expanding our vision we should be
able to gain new insights into human political behavior that,
in turn, should force us to develop a more basic orientation in
our research.

In order to see how Schubert would incorporate a
biopolitical perspective into a model of political behavior, let
us look at three diagrams he has developed. A traditional
paradigm for political behavior is represented in Figure 2.1.
Referring to this as a psychological model, Schubert (1976:177)
argues that "differences in political behavior are explained by
differences in conscious choices as to how to behave, which in
turn are explained by differences in the life experiences of the
actors." In this model it is *only* the social environment and
socially ascribed statuses that have an impact upon cognitive
processes and influence political acts.

A biologically oriented model, as seen in Figure 2.2, is

**Types of Variable Sets:**

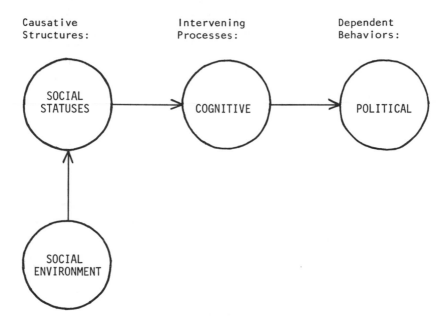

Causative                    Intervening                    Dependent
Structures:                  Processes:                     Behaviors:

SOCIAL
STATUSES          COGNITIVE          POLITICAL

SOCIAL
ENVIRONMENT

FIGURE 2.1    The social science paradigm of political behavior
(Schubert, 1976:177)

somewhat different. Such a model, says Schubert (1976:199),
"directs attention to the nonlogical influences . . . upon all
behavior, and to the hierarchy of survival requirements, the
satisfaction of which is preconditioned to indulgence in
political behavior." According to this model, the basic human
needs in an individual (nutrition, sleep, sex, etc.) interact with
an environment that is both social and natural. Appetitive
behavior takes place when the subject searches the environment
for satisfaction of those needs.

Schubert criticizes both of these models for being incomplete: the traditional social science model looks upon human
behavior as godlike, that is, nonmaterial and exclusively
rational, while the biological model emphasizes the animal

Types of Variable Sets:

| Causitive Structures: | Intervening Processes: | Dependent Behaviors |

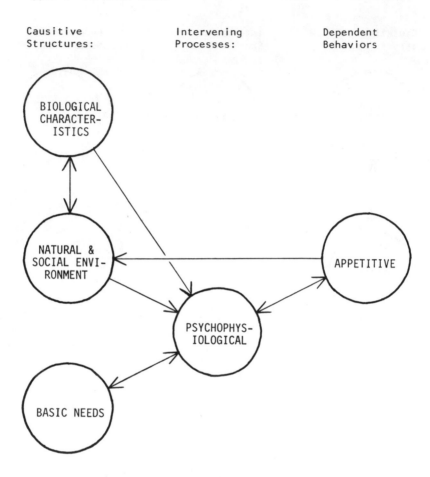

FIGURE 2.2   The biological paradigm of animal behavior
(Schubert 1976:178)

aspects of behavior to the neglect of the cognitive. In place of these two models, Schubert substitutes a combination approach (see Figure 2.3) that looks at the individual as both a rational, knowing creature and as a physical being with

**Types of Variable Sets:**

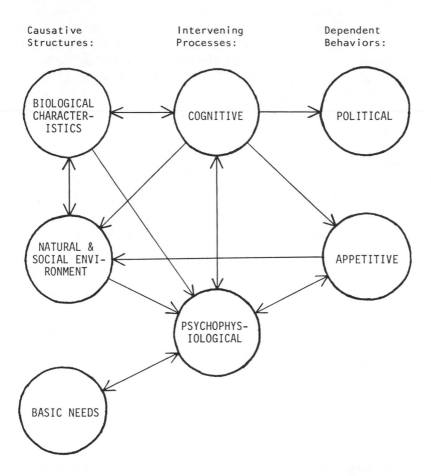

FIGURE 2.3   A life science paradigm of political behavior
(Schubert, 1976:179).

needs, appetites, and biological characteristics.

The life science paradigm faithfully reflects the complex nature of the human species by requiring us to be conscious of the political person as both a knowing, rational actor and as a biological being that is physically bounded. Schubert refers to this as a biosocial model of human behavior that, when applied to the political being, can be described as a model of biopolitical behavior. Modern political scientists ought to heed Schubert's call to explore both the vertical as well as the horizontal relationships diagrammed in Figure 2.3. If that is done, says Schubert (1976:180), we "can deal with political life at the level it is lived and not as an exercise in puns, rhetoric, or intellectual dilettantism."

Schubert's biosocial model of human behavior is the most appropriate model to date for the emerging field of biopolitics. In the succeeding chapters of this volume our discussions will be based on the assumption that, either implicitly or explicitly, this biosocial model forms the theoretical underpinnings of our observations about human biopolitical behavior.

## John C. Wahlke

As a long-time student of political behavior, Wahlke has expressed his perspective on biobehavioral politics in a number of strongly argued writings (1976a, 1976b, and 1978). Wahlke's concern, much like Schubert's, is to "push" the study of political behavior back to the more fundamental questions of political life, which in the recent past have been examined with an incomplete understanding of human nature.

> In spite of the technical and methodological expertise with which individual projects of political-behavior research are generally conducted, collectively they exhibit two serious conceptual shortcomings which severely hamper their capacity to obtain theoretically (or practically) significant results. One is the lack of anchorage in macro-level political theory, i.e., a failure to orient research political behavior by concern for or awareness of any fundamental questions about the state and fate of the polity or the lives and condition of the people in it, or to link up findings about individual behavior to any such concerns, whatever the original motivation for doing the research on it. The other shortcoming is reliance on a [deficient] . . . general behavioral theory, on what earlier political

philosophers would call a flawed conception of human nature
and modern biobehavioral scientists would call an inadequate
and erroneous model of the functioning individual human
organism (Wahlke, 1978:20).

Given these observations, Wahlke feels that the subfield of
political behavior, which is central to the discipline of
political science, has yet to emerge from its prebehavioral
orientation.

In order to comprehend the realities of political life, Wahlke
(1978:20) suggests that we must overcome our "biobehaviorial
illiteracy" by learning "what the 'hard-science' behavioral
disciplines as well as the 'softer' brands of psychology have to
say about human behavior." The knowledge of human nature
to be gained from the life sciences, however, is not a body of
information to be accepted or rejected on the basis of simple
value preferences or whimsy. These sciences have developed
valid and reliable knowledge bases regarding the functioning
of the human organism and political scientists will ignore
them "at their peril." As a matter of simple logic, "the people
whose behavior political scientists study are, after all, no more
exempt from the laws of behavioral dynamics than from the
laws of gravity" (Wahlke, 1978:21).

The incorporation of biological variables into the analysis of
political behavior will not be an especially easy task, but with
an open orientation it should result in a relationship similar to
that of, of example, astronomy to physics and chemistry.

Astronomers know that all the relevant laws and principles of
these two disciplines [physics and chemistry] apply to all the
phenomena which interest astronomers just as they do to any
other physical phenomena. It is not for suggestive analogies or
novel conceptions from which to fashion catchy or transient
speculative theories about planets, stars, galaxies, and meta-
galactic systems that astronomers look to those more basic
sciences, but for established principles about the nature and
behavior of objects in general, taking them as assumptions on
which to build hypotheses about the particular phenomena of
particular interest to them (Wahlke, 1978:21).

In the same manner, political scientists must look to the life sciences as a repository of knowledge that forms the basis for research on the human organism in a political context. If we adopt this perspective, our work will necessarily focus on the fundamental problems of human political life that have long attracted political philosophers. This is so, says Wahlke (1978:28), because "the biobehavioral perspective ... views the phenomena of government and politics from the standpoint of the entire human species, in the context of its evolutionary history." Furthermore, such a perspective "forces us to reexamine our two-dimensional, oversimplified supercognitive social-psychological model of the acting human individual to take into account important uniformities in the behavior of all individuals which are so far ignored by political behavior research."

### Roger Masters

Like Schubert and Wahlke, Masters has reflected broadly on the relationship of biology and politics. And along with them, he articulates the view that social scientists have not been sensitive to the contributions of the life sciences to the study of political life. For example, he states:

> Contemporary biology indicates the untenability of a sharp dichotomy between nature and culture. Although the actions of humans contribute to changes in their physical surroundings, their phenotypes, and their species' gene pool, the physical and biological characteristics of *Homo sapiens* interact with the natural environment throughout individual development and social history. Simplistic assertions that "man makes himself" or "man's innate compulsions are genetic and ineradicable" do not reflect an understanding of the myriad processes involved in human behavior when viewed as a biological phenomenon (Masters, n.d.:24).

Because people interact with the natural environment, political analysts have a responsibility to take this fact into account in their appraisals of political life. Moreover, Masters (n.d.:24-25) suggests five implications of a biological perspective that cannot be ignored.

First, he says, "different aspects of human life must be analyzed with care, without a priori assumptions concerning the presumably 'cultural' or 'natural' status of the causal processes and functional regularities involved." Many phenomena will be found to be neither totally cultural nor exclusively natural, but rather a complex intermingling of the two.

Second, Masters criticizes much of the "sloppy writing" that uses the collective noun "man" without careful definition. It is critical that we make level-of-analysis distinctions between individuals, groups, and the species. What is found to be true at one level of analysis is by no means necessarily true at another.

Third, the evolutionary process of which we are all a part often has its impact in ways that are presently unfathomable. Quoting what has become a classic statement in evolutionary biology—"The chicken is the egg's way of making another egg"—Masters indicates that "the significance of many human events may lie not in the realm of perceived physical consequences on individuals or societies, but in their selective effects on our gene pool." This is consistent with the work of Corning.

Masters's fourth implication is that "the expression of purpose or motivation [which often suffices for political explanation] does not constitute a comprehensive explanation of human phenomena, since from a biological perspective one must explain the existence of human intentions as well as the selective consequences of the means of fulfilling them."

Finally, Masters indicates that political scientists ought to develop a better sense of time, as a biological perspective requires. He sums up this position by suggesting that biology with its open and evolving systems approach provides a better intellectual paradigm for the social sciences than physics with its mechanistic emphasis.

## James C. Davies

The discussion of Roger Masters's work concluded by pointing out his disenchantment with the present systems approach in political science. This critique is Davies's point of departure. He argues:

> With respect to those deeper forces that shape people and institutions in their reciprocal interactions, systems analysis at most and perhaps at best is cartographic: it reads like the maps of railway or postal systems and perhaps electronic circuits, often meticulously describing how things move from point A to point B and join with other things at point C—with little understanding and less appreciation of the forces that initially generate movement and pressure within the systems (Davies, 1975:2).

Davies continues his attack by observing,

> Systems analysis tends to exclude energy, to exclude those things that make a system dynamic and that occasionally cause system overload and failure. Comfortable with that beautifully symmetrical and often empty pair of words—structure and function—systems analysis may be described as dysfunctional. By some writers the causes of that antiseptically described malfunction are politely acknowledged; and then they are ignored, the way Chinese rulers at first ignored the incursions of Europeans into their Central Kingdom. Systems maps include all variables and few explanations, if any (Davies, 1975:2).

Davies is concerned that systems analysts cannot explain change in the political system, particularly in a system that has worked well and then is suddenly rejected by its population. It is "not a banality to say, in order to ascertain what it is within individuals that makes them demand change, we have to get inside individuals" (Davies, 1975:4). In order to do this, Davies repeats, we have "to examine their internal mechanisms, psychologically and biologically." This search for knowledge will require political scientists to probe central nervous and endocrine systems in order to unearth answers about basic political behaviors.

Thus Davies (1975:12) recommends that political scientists get into "the black box that is the very part of the anatomy where all overt behaviors are generated and controlled"—the human organism itself. In Davies's opinion, generalizations about human political behavior have been largely inferential and will never move beyond that until we become more rigorous and more basic in our research. Adopting such an orientation will be difficult for political scientists because they will need biological training well beyond that of an introductory college course.

If political science is to follow Davies's recommendations, studies will have to be designed with care so that certain ethical prerogatives regarding the integrity of the individual are not violated. While a need for caution exists, it does not mean that basic work in the life sciences area cannot be contemplated; it merely means that efforts must be made to ensure the use of proper safeguards.

## *Thomas L. Thorson*

Utilizing what might be termed a philosophically speculative method, Thorson (1970:3) has argued that "man is a part of nature. He acts in his particular environment over time." As a result, "human activity," including politics, "must be understood in terms of what we know about nature and natural processes and, above all, it must be understood as taking place in time." The concept of time is central to Thorson's (1970:3) thinking: "any attempt to understand politics by removing its time dimension creates distortion, often distortion so severe that the attempt ends in failure."

Perhaps Thorson's major contribution is to call attention to the differences in the way classical scholars and modern scholars view Homo sapiens. As stated before, the classical mind looked upon the individual as *in* nature. Human beings function, says Thorson (1970:116), "as a natural phenomenon in the midst of other natural phenomena." In the classical outlook, humanity was never detached from nature, but modern scholars have removed people from nature and described them as looking in from their world. The blame for this orientation, argues Thorson (1970:16), must be placed on the philosopher René Descartes, who in his writings developed the "radical separation of mind from body."

For Thorson (1970:117-118) the critical point is that "politics becomes not as it formerly was, a matter of discovering man's proper place in nature and acting in accordance with it, but a matter of describing objects and *inventing* a way to deal with them. Thus, for example, "it is . . . no accident that the idea of the social contract, which was but a minor theme in classical political thought, becomes a dominant consideration in the wake of the acceptance of the new detached perspective of analysis" (Thorson, 1970:118). Thus, the political scientist has become an inventor who constructs an artifical political reality that takes no account of the individual in nature or the biological characteristics of humanity.

## Criticisms of the Biopolitical Approach

No approach to the study of political science is without criticism. Since biopolitics is relatively new, it is necessarily open to criticism because it challenges accepted paradigms and orientations of the discipline. Those whose ideas are questioned, even implicitly, often react strongly against any suggestion that their particular approach might be found deficient. But in a sense, it's all in a day's work. Scholarship normally does not proceed by applause, but rather by carefully constructed studies that provide answers to well-posed hypotheses. With this in mind, we should look at two critiques of the biopolitical approach, one objective and one with heavy ideological coloring.

The more valuable critique, by Jerone Stephens (1970:707), cautions political scientists to avoid making mistakes by "drawing too facile analogies" between supposed biological principles and the functioning of the political system. Certainly, let us not "use comparisons between body organs and governmental institutions in a metaphorical way" (1970:388). In citing the past errors of the biologist E. V. Cowdry, Stephens abhors the development of analogies that might compare, for example, muscle cells to manual laborers or the nervous system in the body to an intellegentsia. Moreover, we should be cautious about returning to a mistaken social Darwinism that attempted to apply evolutionary principles to man's social behavior.

Stephens echoes other commentators in cautioning political scientists not to become so enamored of biological information that all human behavior becomes reduced to biological imperatives. Human beings are not just rational creatures who think and choose, they are also persons influenced by the mediating effects of social situations. As a subject of political inquiry, Homo sapiens is incredibly complex, and we are only beginning to understand the myriad of factors influencing political life. It is worth emphasizing that not all behavior is purely rational or exclusively situation mediated, but rather that biological factors do indeed influence political activity.

Another element that has concerned Stephens is the ready acceptance by some political commentators of ethological knowledge. Ethology, as previously noted, is the study of evolutionary development of animal behavior. To Stephens (1970:702), generalizations regarding aggression and territoriality, for example, cannot be transferred in toto from ethology and applied to human social behavior. This transference is complex and risky. More will be said about this in Chapter 6, which focuses on the biological aspects of war.

A second critique—one that must be considered ideologically biased—has been offered by Miloslav Formanek, a Marxist social commentator. "The real driving force" underlying the biopolitical thrust, argues Formanek (1976:26), "is the class and political influence of the bureaucratically organized state monopoly capitalism, the endeavor to harness ideology to the interests of this system and to paralyze the revolutionary movement in the capitalist countries, [and] to weaken the role and impact of real socialism." Moreover, bourgeois biologically oriented political scientists "wish to sow confusion within the broad ranks of the working people, while stimulating, motivating, and inciting elements of irrationality of the activity of the masses" (Formanek, 1976:6). Underlying these charges is Formanek's (1976:4) observation that biopolitics is seeking "the roots of mankind's problems in man himself." (It is useful to point out that serious students of biology and politics would be appalled to hear themselves described by Formanek as looking *only* at biological humanity in order to develop solutions to contemporary problems. Schubert's model of biosocial behavior, for example, *combines* in a complex and as yet not well-explored way the biological, social, and cognitive elements that are necessary to objectively explain human behavior. Gently put, Formanek's description of biopolitical research is misleading.)

What concerns Formanek (1976:1), whose view of scholarly inquiry is influenced by ideological considerations, is that biopolitical scholars have been examining a broad range of sources of political behavior "rather than . . . examining social contradictions ensuing from class conflicts." Indeed, argues Formanek (1976:2), "any subordination of social laws to biological laws is nonscientific and socially and politically coextensive with reactionary trends." That is to say that it is "social laws" and only "social laws" that determine human behavior; and of course this observation is perfectly consistent with Marxist ideology. Few responsible scholars today would reduce the explanations of all human behavior to only social factors. This constitutes a social and environmental determinism that is as fallacious as a biological determinism.

Formanek's critique is curious in that it views the wide-ranging scholarship of biopolitics—which, incidentally, he describes as daring—as nothing more than a well-manipulated instrument of capitalist oppression. Clearly, he can offer no evidence of this, nor if he sought it would he find it. Moreover, Formanek grossly misunderstands the nature of open and free scholarship which is continually searching for more accurate appraisals of human nature. His criticisms are simply ideologically based charges unsupported by the normal expectations of evidence as understood by most scholars.

But Formanek is helpful in one respect: we should be

cautious about slipping into any single factor determinism, whether it be "social laws," biological imperatives, or rational calculations. Human beings are much more complex than we have appreciated, and any kind of reductionism distorts their true nature.

## Conclusions

We have seen how a certain disenchantment with the orientations of present day political science led a group of well-known scholars to search for answers about political acitivity in some of the findings of the life sciences. That searching, a central theme of this book, has caused those political scientists to rethink several of the basic premises upon which our understandings of political humanity rest. In doing so, these writers have suggested—each in his own way—that we begin employing models of political behavior that incorporate biological variables along with the normal political variables that we use. Schubert's model of biosocial behavior appears to portray what most of these writers have in mind.

But even more important, the searching has led to numerous imaginative and powerful studies of political behavior during the past several years. It is to these substantive findings that we now turn. We will begin with a discussion of how a biological orientation might assist us in understanding mass political behavior.

## References

Caldwell, L. K. (1964) "Biopolitics: Science, Ethics, and Public Policy." *The Yale Review* 54, 1, October:1-16.

Caldwell, L. K. and W. B. De Ville. (1976) *Science and Social Evolution Implications for Public Policy: A Guide to Advanced Study.* Bloomington: Indiana University.

Corning P. A. (1976) "Toward a Survival Oriented Political Science," in A. Somit, ed., (1976).

―――. (1971) "The Biological Bases of Behavior and Some Implications for Political Analysis." *World Politics,* November.

Davies, J. C. (1975) "Biology and Politics: Wine and Wineskins, Old

and New." Paper presented to the annual convention of the
Midwest Political Science Association, Chicago.

———. (1973) *Human Nature in Politics.* New York: John Wiley &
Sons.

Formanek, M. (1976) "Political Implications of Contemporary Neo-
Biologism." Paper presented to the Tenth Congress of the International Political Science Association, Edinburgh, August 16-21.

Maslow, A. H. (1954) *Motivation and Personality.* New York:
Harper and Row.

———. (1943) "A Theory of Human Motivation." *Psychological Review* 50:370-396.

Masters, R.D. (n.d.) "Politics as a Biological Phenomenon." *Social
Science Information* 14, 2:7-63.

Roberts, M. (1938) *Bio-Politics: An Essay in the Physiology, Pathology, and Politics of the Social and Somatic Organism.*
London: J. M. Dent and Sons.

Schubert, G. (1976) "Politics as a Life Science: How and Why the Impact of Modern Biology Will Revolutionize the Study of Political Behavior," in A. Somit, ed.

———. (1975) "Bio-political Behavioral Theory." *The Political
Science Reviewer* 5, Fall.

Somit, A., ed. (1976) *Biology and Politics.* Paris: Mouton.

———. (1968) "Toward a More Biologically-Oriented Political
Science: Ethology and Psychopharmacology." *Midwest
Journal of Political Science* 12, November:550-567.

Schwartz, D. C. (1974) "Toward a More Relevant and Rigorous Political Science." *Journal of Politics* 36:103-137.

Stephens, J. (1970) "Some Questions About a More Biologically
Oriented Political Science." *Midwest Journal of Political
Science*, November:687-707.

Thorson, T. L. (1970) *Biopolitics.* New York: Holt, Rinehart and
Winston, Inc.

Wahlke, J. C. (1978) "Pre-Behavioralism in Political Science." Presidential address to the annual convention of the American
Political Science Association, New York, September 1.

———. (1976a) "Pre-Behavioralism in Political Science: In Search
of a Dependent Variable." Paper presented to the Tenth Congress of the International Political Science Association,
Edinburgh, August 16-21.

———. (1976b) "Observations on Biopolitical Study," in A. Somit,
ed.

# 3
# Biopolitics and
# The Political System

This chapter examines how biologically oriented political scientists have applied their perspective to aspects of the political system. In doing this we will first discuss a genetic paradigm for political analysis and then move quickly to some innovative evolutionary insights into political authority and rank. A second section of the chapter will describe several tightly focused dimensions of political analysis, public nutrition, social stress, crowding, drugs, opinion surveys, and genetic technology. We begin with some general observations about genetics.

## Genetic Diversity and the Political System

We frequently are reminded that each of us is a unique human being. And we usually respond to this observation with an easy, affirmative nod of the head. But contained within that statement about our uniqueness is a powerful fact of genetic reality. In a genetic sense, (disregarding cloning for the moment), there is no one who is just like us (as individuals). Elliot White (1972) has argued that our individual uniqueness runs counter to the accepted paradigm of the social sciences—that individuals are malleable and manipulable through cultural and political processes. There appears to be an "environmental bias" among social observers that emphasizes the plasticity of Homo sapiens and ignores the genetic character of the species. However, the environmentalist bias is questioned by the vast literature of behavioral genetics. White (1972:1207) advocates a populational approach to studying the political system that "takes individual differences as *the* basic reality and not as deviations from norms that are themselves reified abstractions." This approach takes into account that genetic diversity exists within populations. "The concept of genetic diversity," says White (1972:1209), "implies . . . that individual capacities vary and that beyond a certain point are limited, no matter how favorable the environment."

This approach, however, does not disregard environmental conditions. For example, "children in the West and Japan have indeed been growing taller because of more favorable environmental conditions; but this fact does not preclude a genetically influenced individual variation in height nor genetically imposed limits on future growth" (White, 1972: 1209). As a result, human beings do not have unlimited potential for knowledge, perfection, or activity.

White (1972:1211) cautions that in stating that there are genetic limits to individual capacities, one should not assume that a racist position is being advanced. Indeed, it is those who apply policies across classes or races without understanding genetic diversity who perpetuate the use of stereotypic thinking. "It is unscientific," says White (1972:1212), "to insist a priori on imposing an abstract uniformity on reality."

Having noted genetic diversity, White (1972) puts forward a "populational-interaction paradigm" of the political system. "The genotype—the complete genetic endowment of the individual beginning at conception—predisposes the individual to respond to his environment within a certain range of behavior" (White, 1972:1214-1215). This complete genetic endowment interacts with environmental influences to produce a phenotype. White (1972:1215) diagrams this process quite simply:

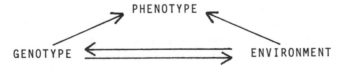

According to White's conceptualization, "individuals with similar genotypes will vary significantly in their phenotypes as a result of environmental differences." This observation accords with the current conceptual basis of modern social science. However, says White (1972:1215), we must take into account "the alternative possibility that within similar environments individuals with varying genotypes will differ accordingly in observed behavior."

While White confesses that he is not at all sure where his paradigm will lead us, he does offer some reflections on the poverty of positions taken by conservatives and liberals who pay no heed to the reality of genetic diversity: "The conservative is stricken with a moral blindness. Readily conceding individual differences in endowment, he yet divests himself of the ethical responsibility to help those who cannot help themselves—or those with ability who, for any reason, have been denied the opportunity to express it" (White, 1972:1241). On the other hand, "The liberal is afflicted with an ideological blindness. Intent on promoting an egalitarian society, he treats everyone toward the bottom of the social heap with the same dosage of medicine" (White, 1972:1241). While these observations describe rather extreme points of view, they give us some insight into several of the underlying assumptions of public policy behavior.

Another author who has explored the impact of genetic considerations as they might affect the general political system—in this case the judicial system—is Fred Kort (1977). Basing his reasoning on the work of Trivers (1971), Kort has inquired whether there might be a biological basis for civil rights and liberties growing out of human reciprocal altruism. He suggests an innovative framework together with several hypotheses that might be utilized in further research. Both White and Kort question whether governmental policies take into account the genetic diversity of the body politic. Indeed, can we make public policies more consistent with the biological and genetic realities of our citizenry? Would such an orientation change the character of those policies?

## Political Authority

In any consideration of the political system, one of the central areas of interest is that of political authority. A normal concern of the political scientist is, "who governs and with what effect?" We routinely look for the locus of power in organizations, bureaucracies, and governments. But because there can be no authority unless there exist those over whom authority is exercised, we also have an interest in the governed. In a rather simple model we can look upon a political system as consisting of the governors and the governed. Ethologists utilize a different terminology to describe a similar relationship in the animal world—dominance-deference hierarchies. Such hierarchical relationships consist of those who dominate behavior and those who acquiesce in or defer to the positions of the dominant.

In reflecting on the nature of political authority, Fred H. Willhoite, Jr. (1976:1110) has theorized that "there seem to be good reasons to believe that man's biological nature incorporates strong propensities to establish and sustain dominance-deference hierarchies within his social groupings; that is, the stratification of political authority, power, and influence may be *by nature* intrinsic to human social existence." Likewise, LaPonce (1978:385) has asserted that "man appears bound to construct hierarchies. . . . Even if man did not either like or need to stratify, society would nevertheless appear to him to be ordered hierarchically." These statements are strikingly different from the commonsense notion that human power relationships and social stratification emerged when ancient agricultural peoples expanded and subdued other groups; the conquered became subservient to the conquerors. Willhoite suggests that contrary to the traditional explanations of the origins of political power, the human species by its very nature includes within itself either a tendency to dominate or be dominated. Let us see how this argument is developed.

Recognizing certain methodological difficulties in his approach and at the same time being conscious of the fact that he is engaging in speculation, Willhoite (1976:1111) indicates that "monkeys and apes are considered to be of great significance for the study of man primarily because they are our nearest evolutionary relatives." Interestingly, whenever scholars have examined the social behavior of primates they have noted dominance-deference relationships that appear to be similar to the familiar political relationships of the human species.

Willhoite (1976:1112-1118) reviews the behavioral character-istics of four primate species: rhesus macaques, savanna-dwelling baboons, gorillas, and chimpanzees. The rhesus macaques create a "central hierarchy" of mature adult males who usually occcupy a central position within a moving group. When conflicts arise between members of the group the dominant males will intervene visually or vocally to prevent further conflict.

Among the savanna-dwelling baboons a male-dominated hierarchy is also in evidence, often with a single or alpha male at the top. When more than one adult male is in the group, a coalition of key adults may be formed that acts as a collective leadership. When threatened by outsiders, the leadership group "takes charge" by confronting the threat and thwarting its success. The authoritative alpha baboons also prevent quar-rels within their group and consequently encourage social stability and tranquility.

Gorillas, very close to human beings in a taxonomic sense, have created a somewhat different type of social and political association. Quite cohesive in its composition, according to Willhoite (1976:1114), the dominance core consists of a single silver-backed male and all of the females and young. The remaining males, both black and silver-backed, adopt per-ipheral roles. "Rank order largely correlates with body size; silver-backed males are dominant over all black-backed males, females, and young. If there are two or more silver-backed males in a group, they are arranged in a linear dominance hierarchy" (Willhoite, 1976:1114). In terms of behavior, "the dominant male in a gorilla group functions as its leader. Every group member seems to be constantly aware of the activity of the 'alpha' male, and cues reflecting a change in the activity of the group are taken from him. Every part of the daily routine—

travel, location of rest stops and feeding places, time and place of nesting—appears to be largely determined by the leader" (Willhoite, 1976:1115). Apparently, among gorillas there is little aggressiveness within the group, and as a consequence the dominant male performs few place-keeping functions.

The final primate species reviewed by Willhoite is the chimpanzee, also a close phylogenetic relative of Homo sapiens. Research on chimpanzees appears to be less definitively established than that of other primate groups but, as Willhoite (1976:1115) points out, one of the interesting findings is that chimpanzees appear to be territorially oriented, i.e., they select a geographic area and more or less stake it out as their own, defending the "borders" with "patrols." As with the other primates discussed, all female chimpanzees are subordinate to mature males. While coalition-type dominance behavior has been noted among chimpanzees, most often a single alpha male will attain a leadership role. However, unlike gorillas, size does not appear to be a major determinant of dominance selection. Rather intelligence and motivation appear to select certain chimpanzees for leadership roles. The reason why intelligent females are selected out is not clear.

What is the meaning of our discussion of primate dominance-deference relationships to an understanding of human political authority? Clearly, the dominance-deference paradigm implies some kind of stratification principle. A few are in positions of power and authority, but most are not. Willhoite's analysis of four primate species develops reasonably good evidence that a "control role," as he terms it, seems common in group-oriented behavior. Moreover, it has been argued by some scholars that aggression within groups seems "to be motivated *primarily* by efforts to preserve established social position and to enforce expected patterns of social behavior" (Bernstein and Gordon, 1974:308, quoted in Willhoite, 1976:1117). What is of interest to us as students of politics is Willhoite's observation that "social order itself—at least among a number of primate species—may be mainly a consequence of individuals' motivations to establish and maintain places for themselves in a dominance-deference rank order." He suggests that the social order of man might also grow out of his very nature. Indeed, it seems probable that Thomas Aquinas' Aristotelian view is correct: "It is natural for man, more than for any other animal, to be a social and political animal, to live in a group. . . . If, then, it is natural for man to live in the society of many, it is necessary that there exist among men some means by which the group may be governed" (Willhoite, 1976:1123).

"Some means" is understood today as a system of government. Quoting Bigelow (1972:6) Willhoite (1976:1120) emphasizes that "human capacities for learning, communications, government, science, and art are products of biological evolution, just as running, or any other manifestation of animal behavior, is an expression of the biological potential of interacting muscles, bones, and nerves." Indeed, in a very strong statement, Willhoite (1976:1120) argues that "we have inherited this readiness to learn dominance-deference behavior and . . . [echoing Bigelow] we still cannot do without effective dominance hierarchies."

With a different biological perspective, LaPonce (1978) has reached a conclusion similar to that of Willhoite. He (1978: 385) asserts that "man is a 'seer' before he is a 'maker' of vertical orderings." This is the result of both physical and physiological considerations. In a physical sense,

> when modern man's ancestors assumed bipedal erect position, the privileged location of *front* became the privileged position *up*. And, since up-down has none of the ambiguity that front and back share with left-right and close-far—a lack of ambiguity due to the fact that gravity orders both self and landscape in terms of up and down, while there is not such congruent ordering of both self and environment on any of the horizontal axes—up-down became man's privileged spatial measure (LaPonce, 1978:387).

The impact of gravity on consciousness is reinforced by physiological factors. "Western culture gives much more attention to the brain, the heart, and the lungs than to the lower organs, if only because, physiologically, man's structure goes from the simplicity of the feet to the complexity of the head" (La Ponce, 1978:389).

Up to this point our discussion has emphasized dominance behavior, but clearly deference or submissive behavior must also be examined. In primate groups deference coexists with dominance, and we have seen that deference is adaptive for tranquillity within the group and for the accomplishment of certain tasks. None of these comments should be interpreted to mean that political hierarchies are exclusively genetic in origin or that most human beings are destined to submit meekly to strong political authority; on the contrary, Willhoite is exceedingly sensitive to such charges. In its simplest form Willhoite's argument states that individuals might have "phylogenetically determined propensities" for leadership, followship, or both. Most of us exist comfortably in dominant or submissive roles. For example, middle children in a family often exercise authority over younger brothers and sisters; but at the same time they defer to the authority of their parents and older siblings. Mayors of cities can dominate political activities within their communities, but they are often called upon to defer or submit to state or national authorities on other matters. It is even possible to suggest that dominant-deferent propensities might lie at the core of the federal principles that undergird American constitutional government.

Given these observations, we can probably agree with Willhoite (1976:1123) that "some kind of dominance will exist in any human society, along with deferential and obedient patterns of behavior." As a matter of fact, "laws and social customs are not unnatural impositions from a source somewhere outside biology. They arise from interactions between the cerebral cortex and other parts of a single body, and from interactions between brains and eyes and ears and vocal cords of different bodies. They are biological results of biological behavior" (Bigelow, 1972:24 in Willhoite, 1976:1126). For humanity then, "the problem is how to prevent political dominance from becoming political domination" (Willhoite, 1976:1126).

## Specific Influences on the Political System

We have looked at how genetic diversity might play a significant role in the construction of public policies, and we have examined an evolutionary-adaptive orientation toward the development of political authority within human societies. Let us now direct our inquiry toward specific factors that might affect general political behavior in contemporary systems.

### Nutrition

While many developing nations wrestle with crippling nutritional deficiencies, in the Western world most problems of nutrition are problems of *overnutrition*. We consume more calories and more protein than are needed for maintaining ourselves in excellent health. As a result inhabitants of advanced societies have developed a peculiar set of illnesses related to overconsumption of food and a sedentary lifestyle.

Apparently there has been little research done relating overnutrition to political behavior, but there has been some interest in the political effects of nutritional impairment in less developed societies (for example, see J. N. Schubert, 1979). This should not be surprising. The less developed nations, essentially in Asia, Africa, and Latin America, lack the resources both to purchase food from abroad and to develop their own efficient agricultural systems. As a result, large numbers of individuals in those societies suffer from malnutrition, shortened life expectancy, and certain associated behavioral difficulties. There are, in the words of Robert B. Stauffer (1969), biological dimensions of political underdevelopment. What might those dimensions be?

Utilizing research findings from a classic, extended experimental study of prolonged semistarvation (Keys, 1950), Stauffer noted two clusters of attitudes that were related to famine conditions. The first is the apathy syndrome he (1969:364-5) describes as "a complex structure of biological and social behavioral responses triggered by reduction in caloric intake. The individual biological dimension includes general weakness, an increase in sleep requirements, ready exhaustion from physical work, a constant sense of tiredness, [and] a feeling of being an 'old man.'" A person who is physically disposed in this way is also a person whose "sense of social efficiency and efficacy" is undermined. In this situation an individual cannot cope with the routine matters of daily life. Quoting Keys (1950:836), Stauffer emphasizes that "men become reluctant to plan activities, to make decisions, and to participate in group activities."

The second attitudinal change noted by Stauffer as resulting from extended semistarvation is an increase in personal irritability. The irritability syndrome consists of an increase in nervousness, self-centeredness, and hostility toward others.

Several additional biological effects of malnutrition are also in evidence. Among these are permanent mental retardation and damage to the central nervous system. Individuals suffering from malnutrition are particularly susceptible to parasitic diseases. In a biological sense the problem of parasites becomes increasingly complex. Stauffer (1969:375) comments that "chronic blood loss of any considerable amount will almost inevitably lead to anemia of a degree sufficient to impair the oxygen-transport of the blood, to lowered tolerance for work, and to increased susceptibility to infections."

Given these considerations, let us now sketch out the disease profile of the citizenry in a less developed nation.

The essential features of the profile that emerge are of a population with a life expectancy less than half that found in the industrialized nations, and with a concentration of high morbidity levels in those diseases that do damage to the very young, as well as in those diseases that persist endemically or cyclically throughout the life of the individual or subject him to prolonged periods of illness. Although some of the diseases in this pattern are exotically tropical, nearly all are also found in temperate and cold climates. What is unique, however, about what can be called the disease syndrome of underdevelopment, is the incidence level of each of these diseases and the manner in which they appear to form a mutually interlocking circle that reinforces underdevelopment. Caloric deficiency lessens the ability of the individual to fight infectious disease: parasitic infections steal food and scarce minerals and vitamins from those affected, thus further weakening the defenses against illness. Infectious diseases and malnutrition make the body less capable of resisting infection by parasites and in coping with the damage done, once contracted. Protein malnutrition in the very young produces permanent physical and mental impairment. It should go without saying that people who begin life severely stunted in body growth and in general central nervous system development are that much less capable of dealing with the relatively hostile biological environment within which they live (Stauffer, 1969:376).

If the great majority of citizens now living in underdeveloped societies are afflicted with the syndrome described above, what is the impact of this situation on the politics of those areas? Stauffer (1969:377-380) lists several important considerations. Visitors from the outside frequently describe people of less developed countries as lazy and indolent, but much of their behavior may have a strong nutritional origin. Some would also charge that such citizens are all too willing to passively accept their fate and are unwilling to take the initiative to dig themselves out of a difficult social predicament. Given the apathy and irritability produced by semistarvation and protein deficiency, the task of nation building as understood by the Western mind seems almost impossible.

Furthermore, to develop real political community requires large numbers of people to make sustained social contributions. Such behavior appears to be exceedingly difficult when the energy levels and intellectual capacities of the citizenry fall short of needs. Moreover, it may be necessary for scholars to rethink the meaning of the concepts of socialization and politicization. As Stauffer (1969:378) explains, "Withdrawn, passive behavior may be socialized into children because the community holds to ideas of normality that have been formed on the basis of how children, suffering from protein deficiency, behave." Because of the mental retardation of children produced by prolonged semistarvation, the achievement norms that have been developed may have to be revised.

It should be pointed out that not all people in the less developed world are lacking in sufficient protein and caloric requirements. Most political and social elites and their children have managed to maintain themselves quite comfortably. A continuation of nutritional deficiencies among the general population, but not among elites and their families, could perpetuate the power positions of elites and forestall the development of democratically based societies.

## The Sedentary Life Style

A quite different range of biologically oriented problems confronts the developed world. Here modern life is permeated with numerous labor-saving devices that have grown out of industrialization and high technology. These developments have spared people a good deal of "sweat" in their personal lives and in their occupational roles. But individuals are physical creatures who need minimal amounts of physical activity in order to sustain their biological constitutions at peak levels of efficiency. So ubiquitous are labor-saving devices that citizens of industrialized nations are prey to a spectrum of illnesses associated with the lack of physical activity. Physicians even call these illnesses the "diseases of civilization"; they include heart disease, stroke, and diabetes.

Along with reduced physical activity comes an apparent increase in psychological stress, tension, and anxiety in modern technologically advanced societies. One possible indicator of this high stress level is the increasing use of tranquilizing drugs, mood elevators, anxiety depressors, and the like.

Is there a relationship between a decrease in physical activity and an increase in psychological stress in advanced industrial societies? The research findings on this question are mixed, though some recent work has linked the passivity of television watching with stress (see Wiegele, 1971).

A clearer example of the relations between physical fitness and psychological balance might be the Tarahumara Indians of northern Mexico, who have developed enormous physical endurance capabilities. West, et al. (1969), indicate that members of the Tarahumara tribe can run unaided and without stopping for over 100 miles. Deer hunting is frequently done by simply chasing the animal until it drops from exhaustion. This superb fitness is accomplished by conditioning rather than by genetic adaptation (Blake and Snow, 1965). Certain social aspects of the Tarahumaras are even more remarkable. "Even though family life is highly structured and local loyalties are fierce, interpersonal or intergroup violence by Tarahumara Indians is almost unknown" (West, et al., 1969:13). Chronic alcoholism, divorce, and stealing are rare within their society. Thus, the presence of high physical endurance capabilities and a particularly favorable psychological climate seem to suggest a correlation between physical fitness and emotional well-being (Wiegele, 1971:58).

If it can be argued that there is evidence of a correlation between physical fitness and the incidence of tension and anxiety in individuals and groups, can we then look for a partial explanation of societal tension, turmoil, and instability in the general physical unfitness of modern, technologically advanced societies? Perhaps. We do know that revolutionary activity most often begins and grows in an urban setting. Those living in cities have a tendency to be less physically fit than those living in rural areas. It is possible that the unfit are more prone to tension-stimulated behavior.

The physical fitness of political elites may also be a significant factor in determining leadership behavior. If research can demonstrate a correlation between the level of fitness of a decision maker or a decision group and the type of decision rendered—for example, one that promotes conflict resolution or one that intensifies or expands conflict—then we may have isolated an important variable in the decision-making process.

Some of the hypothetical associations that have just been suggested might be easily tested. In the United States a good deal of medical and epidemiologic data exist that could be correlated with political conflict data. Infant mortality data, often described as the best single statistical indicator of health, could easily be correlated with a broad range of political variables. If some of this research is accomplished, we will not only have a better understanding of the sedentary life style that contributes to physical unfitness, we might also gain insights into several broader questions of human social/political behavior.

*Social Stress*

Looking at the political system in broad terms, James C. Davies (1976:98) has observed what he calls a certain "wave-like quality" about system-wide social and political events. Societies normally go through relatively long periods in which change is orderly, slow, and developmental. But for some as yet unexplained reason, these same societies "rather suddenly and very surprisingly enter periods in which development is gross, intense, and often enduring" (Davies, 1976:98). Following this kind of a "flare-up," there is a return to an earlier slower-paced development. What intrigues Davies are the causes of the sudden and intense flare-ups. Why do they happen? And why do they occur in seemingly rhythmic fashion? True, says Davies, we know a good deal about the cultural forces that induce and influence these changes; but, in the final analysis, it is "the set of forces within human beings" themselves that really give rise to these profound social and political changes.

How does Davies connect what goes on inside individuals and what happens outside of them in the broad social system? His interesting argument first notes that

> despite the big conceptual gap between two closely linked kinds of act—private and public—there occurs, at certain junctures in history, collective violence that involves hundreds, thousands, and even millions of individuals. And the events taking place within the individual central control system of each human actor so involved in such collective action, from childhood on to adulthood, are a necessary component of vast "social" processes studied by political scientists. . . . *Concerted* violence of a *very complex and enduring sort* that sometimes occurs in human societies is absent in perhaps all other animal societies. This complexity and this duration correlate with the degree of development of the neocortex [in the brain of] . . . Homo sapiens (1976:104).

Even more astounding, says Davies, is that

> there is such remarkable specificity of joint political action in

times of major change (nonviolent or violent) that, despite the spillover of public and private events into each other, there must be remarkable circuit specificity among the billions of neurons that extend through the major segments of the central control systems of the thousands and millions of individuals who collaborate in such gigantic public events (1976:106).

These "gigantic public events" constitute what might be called periods of grave social stress or pressure. Some examples might include a revolution, concerted economic activity, or political demonstrations. In Davies's conceptualization it appears that stress is the linkage between the public and the private. Thus, "the process by which the organism deals with tension [stress] involves an intimate and usually orderly interaction between the firing of nerves and the secretion of hormones." Moreover, "the response to stress indeed empha-sizes the neurochemical interdependence and the interaction of the nerve centers and endocrine glands" (Davies, 1976:116).

In what he refers to as a prototheory, Davies (1976:102) attempts to tie all of these comments together in a succinct package:

When there has been a long-term accumulation of demands within the human organism and this accumulation is conjoined with environmental inputs of two kinds (first inhibitors and then releasers), there is a rather sudden, intense, and rapid release (discharge) of minute amounts of energy stored in special-function particles in memory neurons in the neocortex, where the relatively long-term accumulation of energy has taken place. This accumulation of ionized particles . . . is thus located in the neural substrate of complex, emotion-laden memory. The discharge of these ionized particles within memory neurons is a crucial link in the affective response to the frustration of basic drives. This sudden, intense, and rapid discharge involves activation of and feedback from higher energy circuits in the paleocortex and the midbrain and the hypothalamus. This discharge is an essential component of both small and large changes in the environment, including the political system.

Clearly, Davies's prototheory gets us into the "black box"

that we alluded to in Chapter 2. The questions he raises are incredibly complex; but if the analyst wants to get beyond simple inferences or armchair theorizing he must adopt imaginative hypotheses that go to the core of human political behavior. But this prototheory of social and political turmoil probably can be simplified and clarified a bit.

The part of the brain that stores and processes information is located in the neocortex. Human memories, especially those with high emotional content, are stored in the neocortex. This storing takes place physiologically by locking into the brain structure ionized (or electrically charged) particles. These "ions of emotion" (the particles) can be activated by events that are either internal or external to the person. The ions, through electricity, carry signals to other parts of the brain and to the endocrine glands. This process of activating endocrine glands releases chemicals into the blood stream, which activates the human body by making it more alert and primed for activity. When this priming and alerting process achieves a sufficient threshold in a large number of individuals, the physiological stage has been set for some type of flare-up. If a low threshold has been crossed, the flare-up might be only a peaceful demonstration of some type. But if a higher threshold is breeched, that is, if the endocrine system and brain have been exceedingly activated, then it is possible that group violence, revolution, or war might occur.

We alluded above to two other aspects of Davies's prototheory. Not only is Davies interested in the rhythms of social events, he is also concerned with the commonality of social behavior and the specificity of the objects of that behavior. In sharing basic human needs, people will often have similar orientations to social-political events such as the American Revolution. These orientations frequently result in shared frustrations. Thus, because of shared experiences over time, a single social group, Davies claims, will store similar memory ions that are prone to be released after a particular threshold has been crossed. Also, because of similar history (i.e., memory), specific objects of violence might also be shared.

Keep in mind that Davies's prototheory is being offered only as an untested hypothesis; no claim for truth is being made (Davies, 1976:105). For example, at this point in the development of our knowledge we do not really know what memory ions are. We do not know whether their release in and of itself is sufficient to stimulate violence. Furthermore, the interaction of the ions, the brain, the endocrine system, and human political behavior is yet to be empirically tested. In short, Davies has presented us with an imaginative and perceptive way to develop hypotheses about the ebb and flow of collective political behavior that have evaded us in the past. It is to be hoped that biopolitical researchers will be able to test this perceptive model in the near future.

## Crowding and Political Aggression

In our examination of factors that may influence mass political behavior, we should not overlook the impact of crowding. In our daily living all of us have at some time felt the effect of crowding whether it be at a private party, a department store, an athletic event, or a busy street. Crowding somehow makes us feel uncomfortable, and we are greatly relieved when we can escape into a less crowded atmosphere.

Because of the apparently negative feelings produced by crowding, Susan Welch and Alan Booth hypothesized that crowding might be a factor in promoting political aggression. Many studies have identified crowding as related to aggression in animal populations. Other studies have looked at the effects of crowding in human societies and some relationships were found between crowding and juvenile delinquency, mental disorders, and crime.

According to Welch and Booth (n.d.:152), there are two dimensions to crowding: it can be looked at in terms of an individual's household, or in terms of density of population in a neighborhood. "A person living in a crowded household is constantly subject to the demands of others. He must compete with others for space and facilities to pursue his own goals." Moreover, "his surroundings are more likely to be noisy and he is much less likely to have privacy than someone who lives in relatively uncrowded surroundings." But more importantly, an individual living in a crowded household may find such conditions psychologically frustrating and stressful. "This stress is exaggerated,"say Welch and Booth, "if, in addition to a crowded household, an individual lives in a crowded neighborhood environment." In the latter case, an individual might become a victim of sensory overload as a result of seeing too many people, hearing too many noises, and becoming frustrated by too many situations.

Our interest, of course, is the effect of crowding on politically oriented aggression. This association, as Welch and Booth (n.d.:153) indicate, is really quite logical. After all, "large numbers of people living in a relatively small area are more readily available for mobilization once a disorder starts, particularly if they are already disposed toward aggression." Contacts and communications between people in congested situations are facilitated by the fact of simple proximity. And proximity means, in a practical sense, availability for involvement if some kind of "outdoor happening" appears probable. Furthermore, Welch and Booth (n.d.:153) indicate that "high density may contribute to civil disorder by making surveillance of the population and control of incidents more difficult. An incident between a policeman and a civilian might be easy to control with only a few people around, but extremely difficult when hundreds of people are observing the action."

With these observations in mind, Welch and Booth hypothesized that individuals living in crowded conditions would seek a release from their stressful environment by being aggressive, possibly even politically aggressive. In order to test this hypothesis, data were gathered on civil disorders in sixty-five nations. Measures of crowding (in both households and geographic areas) were correlated with measures of social turmoil such as riots, demonstrations, terrorism, and human casualties. Other variables were also included.

Welch and Booth (n.d.:155) found "that household crowding and to a lesser extent areal density . . . [accounted] for moderate amounts of variance in this type [demonstrations, etc.] of political aggression." The number of people per room in a household, an important measure of density, was the single most important variable in linking crowding to political violence. While Welch and Booth are aware that their findings are preliminary, they speculated that there is a discernible relationship between the way people feel because of being crowded and their tendency to act aggressively within the political system. These findings should help us to locate crowding thresholds that could predict the onset of civil strife in some areas and societies.

## Drugs

Related to the question of civil order is the accelerated use of drugs in many contemporary societies. So much has been written about psychoactive drugs and their social consequences during the past ten to fifteen years that there appears to be little need to review that work. Observers should be cautioned, however, that much of this writing is pejorative and biased either in favor of the political system or against it. It is frequently difficult to thread one's way through such material to an objective appraisal.

Clearly, political scientists have paid little attention to the political impact of drug use and abuse within the larger political system. This is not the case with sociologists, anthropologists, and psychologists, who have engaged in rigorously scientific research to study the causes of drug dependency and the most workable methods of treatment and rehabilitation for individuals who have become addicted. But, in general, we do not have a good fund of information about how drugs might influence mass political behavior.

One noteworthy exception to this situation is the work of Robert B. Stauffer (1971). In writing about the role of drugs in political change, Stauffer has very carefully described the potential political impact of excess usage of depressants, stimulants, and hallucinogens. Bear in mind that "while much of the literature on drugs supports the conclusion that cultural controls determine how individuals react, and hence define effects, this conclusion should not obscure the fact that distinct physiological effects follow from specific drugs" (Stauffer, 1971:9).

Alcohol is a depressant widely used in industrial societies.

The percentage of users who eventually become addicted to alcohol is between 2 and 10 percent. According to Stauffer (1971: 9), the alcoholic "can be expected to have developed a retreatist personality, to have one or more physical signs of deterioration, and to suffer one or another of the psychic manifestations of the disease: paranoia, acute hallucinosis, delirium tremens, or Korsakoff's psychosis."

Users of depressants are also known to have high suicide rates, which appear to reflect an inwardly-directed hostility. In his cross-cultural studies of alcohol abuse Stauffer (1971:10, note 3) cites one of McClelland's (1971:41, 78) findings regarding societies in which alcohol consumption might be considered excessive. Folk tales "from heavy-drinking societies contained more references to hunting, sharp implements (arrow, spear, and knife) and violent physical manipulation (cut, chop, stab)."

The political impact of the overuse of depressants produces "personality changes in the direction of withdrawal from involvement in the political life of the society, a decrease in the sense of political efficacy in all forms of political participation, and increases in feelings of alienation, cynicism, and mild paranoia" (Stauffer, 1971:10, note 3). With regard to alcoholism specifically, if up to 10 percent of its users become addicted, such a substantial group of "dropouts" could have consequences for the political process. Moreover, the families of alcholics are also influenced and their concerns are deflected from involvement in the major issues of politics and into family-centered therapeutic services (Stauffer, 1971:10).

Stimulants, especially amphetamines, can also influence political behavior. Excessive use of amphetamines "produces rapid mood changes, the most important being the development of paranoid symptoms. The user is also driven to compulsive activity, to excessive verbosity, becomes anxious, irritable, and may suffer from auditory hallucinations. . . . Repeated periods of paranoia coupled with the other symptoms . . . remove users from any possible effectiveness in politics, destroy all basis for political community, and could easily lead, should such individuals momentarily become caught up in a political scene—a demonstration, for example—to a ready resort to politically pointless violence" (Stauffer, 1971:11).

Hallucinogens, while sharing some of the characteristics of depressants, are quite different from stimulants in their effects. The passivity and lethargy normally associated with hallucinogens could also have a political effect. Modern political systems, especially democratic systems, require complicated relationships between citizens and governmental offices and bureaucracies. Citizens who might be withdrawn and lethargic cannot be politically effective within such a demanding social milieu. Hallucinogens, such as marijuana and the more potent LSD, produce what Stauffer calls a "spectator ego." Because participation is a fundamental ingredient of democracy, an increase in the number of passive citizens could undermine the long-term viability of political freedom.

This latter thought is also prominent in the work of Dean Jaros (1972), who was concerned about the effect of tranquilizers on political behavior. In indicating that most people acquire their basic political orientations as children and that such orientations become a relatively enduring part of each individual's political outlook, Jaros asked whether persons might become temporarily desocialized by chemical means. He put the hypothesis in this fashion: "Depressants (by decreasing discriminative ability) should modify the substantive nature of political choices made by citizens" (Jaros, 1972:8).

In an impressively rigorous experimental design utilizing University of Kentucky undergraduate students as subjects, Jaros proceeded to test this and other hypotheses. A commonly prescribed tranquilizer, pentobarbital, was administered in differing doses to seventy-seven volunteers. Subjects were asked to perform various tests after having ingested the pentobarbital. As is so often the case with social science research, no strong relationships were found by this experiment. Jaros (1972:27) observes that "since depressants impair discriminative abilities, drugged subjects should have shown a preference for grosser political alternatives. Modest relationships supporting this premise were . . . revealed." Even though these findings must be described as limited, the creativeness of the research effort clearly indicates that much more intensive studies ought to be undertaken.

Stauffer has also called for further research, though of a different kind. "Work on the interrelationships between drug use and the formation of antisystem groups has utility in the study of recruitment into such movements, the dialectics that sustain and increase in-group loyalty and membership, and the consequences of policies adopted by the larger political community in response to the perceived threat" (Stauffer, 1971:21). In assessing the amount of basic research that will be required to provide political scientists with a good grasp on the political influence of drug usage, we can say only that Stauffer and Jaros have made a good start. Furthermore, we have seen how two political scientists have examined the use of drugs that might threaten the social order of democratic systems; we have not examined how drugs might be utilized by governments to enhance social control. This is another topic that deserves extended study by political analysts.

## Public Opinion Surveys

Much information about the political attitudes of citizens in a democracy is gained from political surveys. Such surveys are typically commissioned by political candidates, television stations, newspapers, and independent pollsters.

Most public opinion surveys involve a situation in which a questioner (the poll taker) asks subjects (respondents) what their opinions happen to be regarding a particular topic of public interest. The subject provides a verbal response that is duly noted by the poll taker. Data from a large group of subjects is aggregated and analyzed, then judgments regarding the state of the public mind and actions likely to result from such public attitudes are predicted. These polling practices have been widespread in most open societies for at least the past thirty years.

One of the common assumptions underlying these opinion surveys, especially as they relate to elections, is that people with certain kinds of attitudes will engage in certain kinds of behaviors. Criticizing this assumption, Wahlke and Lodge (1972:508) argue that "experiments on attitude change and congruence have demonstrated repeatedly that the correspondence between behavioral components is rarely if ever one-to-one; it is in fact generally low-to-moderate. Hence, to rely on any one component as a single indicator of attitude or behavior, as is the common practice in political survey research, is conceptually untenable." Their critique of opinion surveys proceeds to what they consider a more serious flaw.

Leaving aside the fact that verbal behavior is in a large part subject to conscious control with all the attendant risks of deliberately incomplete, misleading, or flagrantly erroneous reports, respondents with the best will in the world may produce unreliable or invalid verbal data when they attempt to report on any of the supposed components of behavior—cognitive, affective, or overtly actional. To use data this way wrongly assumes that human beings are able to discern intellectually either the cognitive structure of their perceptions or the kind and intensity of emotions they are actually experiencing, and that their *post-facto* recollections of them are dependable evidence about their past experiences. It also assumes contrary to evidence that most of the emotional reactions people experience occur on a verbal level. Finally, again without empirical support, it assumes that people are all by and large equal in ability and talents for introspectively assessing and verbally reporting their feelings (Wahlke and Lodge, 1972:508).

While Wahlke and Lodge do not reject verbally reported data, they insist that researchers will have more confidence in their judgments if they adopt a multiple-indicator approach. They regard psychophysiological measures as among the most promising, particularly since they lend themselves to an experimental orientation.

The study of psychophysiology examines several of the bodily processes that are homeostatically regulated by the autonomic nervous system (ANS). These processes include the regulation of heart rate, breathing, body temperature and chemistry, and skin conductance. People who perceive stimuli from the environment will not only engage certain cognitive processes, but their bodies will also react in a variety of ways depending upon the nature of the stimulus and the way it is perceived. For example, the heart will beat considerably faster in a person who is frightened and adrenalin will be released into the bloodstream in preparation for emergency behavior.

Utilizing the knowledge that an individual can react verbally to a stimulus coming from the environment *and* physiologically as described above, Wahlke and Lodge (1972) devised an ingenious multiple-indicator experiment. Subjects were seated in an isolated room and shown a series of slides depicting politically relevant information regarding "poverty, air and water pollution, crime, civil strife, unemployment, racial disorder, assassinations, confrontations, demonstrations, etc." They were asked to record their reactions to each of the slides by pushing a button on a switch box that corresponded to a typical five-point verbal-report scale labelled strongly agree or highly favorable, agree or favorable, neutral or don't care, disagree or unfavorable, strongly disagree or highly unfavorable. At the same time that these responses were being given, electronic instruments were continuously recording four physiological measures: heart rate, relative carotid pulse pressure, galvanic skin conductance, and electrocardiogram data.

The study generated numerous findings, but only a few of them need to be reported here in order to illustrate the nature of the research. For example, "both heart rate and pulse pressure reactions suggest that the respondents are more reactive to stimuli containing racial (Black) content than they verbally report. . . . On the other hand, the data suggest that respondents are less affected by stimuli relating to political efficacy, to political authoritarianism, and to civil disorder, than they verbally report" (Wahlke and Lodge, 1972:518).

Two general conclusions are notable. "It appears," Wahlke and Lodge (1972:518) state, "that verbal-physiological incongruity occurs primarily on those stimuli with strong emotive connotations, e.g. the words 'Law and Order,' 'America: Love It or Leave It.' All in all, the verbal responses tend to exhibit highly structured patterns, while the addition of physiological measures appear to add another dimension, basically emotive underpinning for the verbal responses." Secondly, "the ability to verbalize the strength of one's likes and dislikes may well not be randomly distributed in a population. If true, the reliance on verbal self-report introduces a systematic bias into social science research" (Wahlke and Lodge, 1972:520).

The study represents a preliminary effort not only to test several hypotheses relating to the substance of political behavior but also to explore the usefulness of multiple physiological measurement techniques. "In many instances during this experiment," report Walhlke and Lodge (1972: 527), "verbal self-report alone would have provided incomplete, if not misleading or erroneous information about the actual behavioral consequences of exposure to a given stimulus." So promising has this research thrust become that a broad range of studies has been produced by the "Stony Brook group." These include Lodge, Cross, Tursky and Tanenhaus (1975); Lodge, Cross, Tursky, Tanenhaus, and Reeder (1976); Lodge, Tanenhaus, Cross, Tursky, Foley, and Foley (1976); and Tursky, Lodge, Foley, Reeder, and Foley (1976).

## Genetic Technology

As technological innovation proceeds virtually unchecked through the twentieth century, many writers have pointed out that our capacity to deal with the moral and political challenges posed by technology appears to be falling hopelessly short of what is required. Perhaps in no field is this assertion more relevant than that of genetics. Blank (1977:1) has observed that "as theoretical knowledge is transformed into practice, traditional political concepts, such as individual rights and the common good, will demand an increasing need for reformulation." Unfortunately, very little rigorous and/or intensive work by political scientists has been addressed to the policy-oriented challenges of genetic research.

Political philosophers, however, have for centuries reflected on questions that explored the relationship between the rights of individuals and those of society generally. There is no need here to review the extended history of such scholarship. But it is important that several questions be introduced into our considerations so that we will become aware of the seriousness of current genetic issues.

Because genetic manipulations can have a long-term impact on the development of a species, we must inquire as to the rights of future generations. Must human behavior at this point in time reflect a concern for the unborn, say fifty years hence? "Experiments involving the manipulation of genes may enable persons in the future to produce their own insulin or may even eliminate genetic diseases as we know them today. But they may also produce new forms of life which might threaten the health and survival of the human species" (Abbott and Frankel, 1977:11). How should a political system respond to the challenges posed by the manipulation of genetic material? Should such research be banned by legislative fiat (see Committee of the Life Sciences and Social Policy, 1977)?

Much of the popular dialogue on genetic manipulation involves speculation as to whether it might be possible to create an "ideal" human genotype. The opening section of this chapter called attention to the reality of genetic diversity on this planet. Most biologists would agree that any effort to channel genetic manipulations toward some predetermined end will result in either serious difficulty or catastrophe, since it is with genetic diversity that man is prepared best for adaptation to changing environments.

Moreover, it is virtually impossible to determine the long-term impact of genetic decisions made now. Nor can we predict the nature of the human environment a hundred or a thousand years hence. On the other hand, we are not without our obligations to posterity. According to Keiffer, "as a minimum, the living have an obligation to refrain from actions that would endanger future generations' enjoyment of the same rights that the living now enjoy. Proper moral concern is not limited to the 'near neighbor,' but also the 'distant neighbor' in space and time" (quoted in Blank, 1977:13).

But genetic questions become even more complex when one applies what Blank (1977:14) calls "strictly utilitarian criteria to any trade-off between individual rights and societal needs."

He asks, "where is the utility to society in keeping a trisomic-21 [a mongoloid] alive at a [lifetime] cost of approximately $250,000? On a strictly cost-benefit basis there is probably none. More crucial is [the question] what right does society have to make abortion compulsory in the case of a mongoloid fetus? . . . The individual rights and moral discretion of the parents in the case of the mongoloid fetus . . . [are] directly in conflict with the utilitarian needs of society."

Furthermore, and this is a point of heated debate among geneticists, genetic disorders appear to be spreading in the human species. One factor that accounts for this apparent increased distribution is the developing technology of health and medicine that is able to keep those with genetic defects not only alive but also able to reproduce.

It is in the various aspects of genetic screening, however, that several issues dealing with individual rights vs. common good conflicts come strongly into focus. Blank (1978:16-20) has described these issues in detail. Matters relating to rights often enter the public policy realm through mandatory screening programs of which there are two types. The first type attempts to detect genetic disabilities in individuals so that therapeutic treatment might commence. A good example of this type is the screening of newborns to detect the presence of phenylketonuria (PKU), a disease that results in severe mental retardation if untreated. However, with proper dietary treatment beginning soon after birth, the effects of PKU can be averted, and the individual will develop normally. This type of screening "when combined with treatment of affected individuals, could be justified as a means of saving public funds. The compulsory screening element might be supported by the 'parens patriae' doctrine that the state can act to protect those that cannot protect themselves." Certain conflicts with religious beliefs are yet to be resolved with regard to PKU screening.

The second type of mandatory screening, according to Blank, attempts "to identify carriers of recessive deleterious genes and inform them of the risk of bearing children with genetic diseases if their spouse is also so identified." Screening for the presence of sickle cell anemia falls into this category. If the state mandates such carrier screening, its purpose no doubt would be to shape the reproductive decisions of sickling parents. It is difficult to justify governmental intrusion into such private decisions. Furthermore, Blank (1978:11) points out that even voluntary screening programs might be suspect because of the social stigma attached to being a carrier of a disease such as sickle cell anemia. He indicates that carriers fear discrimination by insurance companies and possibly even employers if their carrier status is made known.

Mandatory screening that does not include preventative treatment, as in the case of PKU, could have far from subtle influences on decisions made by citizens. For example, consider the case of a woman who is informed on the basis of a mandatory screening program that she is carrying a mongoloid fetus. Governmental influences might be brought to bear on her that would, in effect, eliminate her freedom of choice. It does not stretch the imagination to foresee a "public service" announcement on television encouraging prospective parents to abort a mongoloid fetus for the good of society whose financial resources and specialized care facilities are not adequate for treatment. Further, public attitudes will be shaped by such TV announcements and, if the parents decide to bring the fetus to full term, the parental decision might be derisively received by much of society, thereby stigmatizing not only the parents but also the child. Thus, it would be difficult to maintain individual moral prescriptions in the face of concerted governmental "suggestion." It is the existence of a screening program, however, that gives government information that can be transformed into social influences to shape private child-bearing decisions. (For information on public policy relating to human experimentation, see Stephens, 1975.) Ironically, "by providing fully informed freedom of choice [to parents], then, advances in genetic screening might result in the abrogation of such freedom" (Blank, 1977:23).

If genetic screening became universal, a wealth of information, regarding genotypes might become available. Eugenics, which justifiably arouses negative feelings in most people because of activities in Nazi Germany, can be described as the study of genetically improving the human species. Negative eugenics attempts to prevent the incidence of certain handicaps that are genetically transmitted. Positive eugenics seeks to enhance the propagation of "desirable" human qualities such as beauty and intelligence. As Blank (1977:25) indicates, "at the core of eugenics, positive or negative, is the issue of the rights of people to reproduce as they desire." There are numerous further ethical complexities that must be dealt with in any consideration of eugenics.

Genetic information about an individual must be considered as private information. Are rights of privacy violated when the government collects such information? Who defines "desirable" traits? Who chooses the traits to be selected? What will be the impact of today's selections on future generations?

While many observers find the issues raised by eugenics tinged with racism and elitism, Blank (1977:25) warns that "as technology in these genetic areas grows more complex and the earth becomes more crowded, the pressures to adopt positive eugenics will probably increase." Few solutions are available at the present time to the problems posed by an effort to control the human genotype.

Further problems seem to be virtually upon us with regard to the awesome possibility to clone human beings. Cloning "is a process by which the original nucleus of an egg with its genetic code is removed and replaced with a nucleus from a body (somatic) cell" (Blank, 1977:26). The resulting manipulated egg can then be artifically implanted in a womb. The birth resulting from such an implantation is a perfect genetic duplicate of the organism from which the nucleus was taken. Much work has already been done regarding the cloning of animals; and it is predicted that eventually cloning will have a revolutionary effect on agriculture and animal husbandry. While humans apparently have never been cloned, scientists believe that such a capability is an eventual certainty.

Several social/political issues are raised by the possibility of cloning human beings. The basic question, of course, is: to clone or not to clone? Quoting Kass (1971), Blank (1977:27) states that "among sensible men, the ability to clone a man would not be a sufficient reason for doing so. Indeed, among sensible men there would be no human cloning." Others have taken a much more pragmatic position and argued that if outstanding individuals are identified, the human species would profit by producing numerous replicas. We are doubtless approaching the point at which political authorities will be forced to respond to this apparent dilemma.

If, however, societies ultimately allow the cloning of human beings to proceed, the question of the political rights of the clone comes immediately to the forefront. Blank (1977:28) indicates that if the clone "is simply a biological extension of a donor, an exact copy of an existing genotype," it is conceivable that he might not be considered an individual in the sense understood by Western jurisprudence. What if a clone were created for the purpose of providing transplantable replacement organs for the original donor? Does a clone have a right to his own body? Or is that body little more than an organ warehouse that can be exploited at will?

What rights are to be accorded to the grossly abnormal creatures that will result from inevitable errors in the cloning process (Blank, 1977)? Will such creatures have a *human* nature? What political rights will they have? Will they be allowed to vote? What will be the political result of intentionally cloning for subhuman characteristics? Will such subhumans form a new class that will influence the political process in as yet unknown ways? Could we clone for a class of low mentality slaves? How might the prohibition of slavery in the U.S. Constitution apply to slave clones?

At the other end of the spectrum, will those cloned for intellectual, artistic, or political brilliance form an aristocratic new class? Certainly such clones, because of their outstanding qualities, will be able to exert a disproportionately greater influence on political processes than "normal" human beings.

Many, though not all, of the questions just raised could be solved politically by keeping the number of clones at a minimum. However, the juridical questions regarding rights and responsibilities must be faced as soon as the first human is cloned. Further, there are moral and ethical issues brought forward by genetic technology that relate not only to cloning but also to larger questions of species survival. As Hartigan (1978) has suggested, ethical prescriptions might have to be reexamined in the light of human biological origins.

## Conclusions

We have seen how a reasonably broad range of biologically related factors can exert influences, directly or indirectly, on the general political system. Such research has been difficult for political scientists to perform, but progress is clearly being made. An awareness of the relationships between biological factors and mass political behaviors should alert decision makers to the necessity of incorporating biological considerations into their public policy choices.

We turn now to an examination of how biological factors influence the behavior of individual political elites.

## References

Abbott, P. and M. S. Frankel. (1977) "Genetic Technology and Intergenerational Justice: A Preliminary Inquiry." Paper presented to the annual convention of the Southwestern Social/Political Science Association, Dallas, April 30–March 2.

Bernstein, I. S. and T. P. Gordon. (1974) "The Function of Aggression in Primate Societies." *American Scientist* 62, May-June.

Bigelow, R. (1972) "The Evolution of Cooperation, Aggression, and Self-Control," in J. K. Cole and D. D. Jensen, eds., *Nebraska Symposium on Motivation*. Lincoln: University of Nebraska Press.

Blake, B. and C. Snow. (1965) "Anthropological and Physiological Observations on Tarahumara Endurance Runners." *American Journal of Physical Anthropology* 23, September: 293-301.

Blank, R. (1978) "Public Policy Implications of Human Genetic Technology: Genetic Screening." Paper presented to the annual convention of the Western Political Science Association, Los Angeles, March.

(1977) "Political Implications of Genetics Research: Individual Rights and the Common Good." Paper presented to the annual meeting of the American Political Science Association, Washington, D.C., September.

Committee of the Life Sciences and Social Policy, National Academy of Sciences. (1977). *Assessing Biomedical Technologies: An Inquiry into the Nature of the Process*. Washington, D.C.: U.S. Government Printing Office.

Davies, J. (1976) "Ions of Emotion and Political Behavior: A Prototheory," in A. Somit, ed., pp. 97-125.

Hartigan, R. S. (1978) "Nature, Man, and Morality: A Naturalistic Ethic." Paper presented to the annual meeting of the Conference for the Study of Political Thought, Loyola University of Chicago, April 7-9.

Jaros, D. (1972) "Biochemical Desocialization: Depressants and Political Behavior." *Midwest Journal of Political Science*, February:1-28.

Kass, L. (1971) "The New Biology: What Price Relieving Man's Estate?" *Science*, November 19:779-788.

Keys, A. et al. (1950) *The Biology of Human Starvation*. Minneapolis: University of Minnesota Press.

Kort, F. (1977) "A Biological Basis of Civil Rights and Liberties: Another Perspective of Preferred Freedoms and Justice as Fairness." Paper presented to the annual convention of the Midwest Political Science Association, Chicago, April 21-23.

LaPonce, J. A. (1978) "Relating Biological, Physical, and Political Phenomena, The Case of Up and Down." *Social Science Information* 17, 3:385-397.

Lodge, M., D. Cross, B. Tursky, J. Tanenhaus and R. Reeder. (1976) "The Psychophysical Scaling of Political Support in the 'Real World'." *Political Methodology*:159-182.

Lodge, M., J. Tanenhaus, D. Cross, B. Tursky, M. Foley and H. Foley. (1976) "The Calibration and Cross-Model Validation of Ratio Scales of Political Opinion in Survey Research." *Social Science Research*, December 5:325-347.

Lodge, M., D. Cross, B. Tursky, and J. Tanenhaus. (1975) "The Psychophysical Scaling and Validation of a Political Support Scale." *American Journal of Political Science* 19, 4, November:611-649.

McClelland, D. C. (1971) "The Power of Positive Drinking." *Psychology Today* 4, January:40 ff.

Schubert, J. N. (1979) "Biopolitics and World Malnutrition." Paper presented to the annual convention of the International Studies Association, Toronto, March.

Somit, A. (1976) *Biology and Politics*. Paris: Mouton.

Stauffer, R. (1971) *The Role of Drugs in Political Change*. New York: General Learning Press.

————. (1969) "The Biopolitics of Underdevelopment." *Comparative Political Studies* 2, 3, October:361-387.

Stephens, J. (1975) "Medical Experiments on Humans and the Need for a Public Policy," in M. Holden, Jr. and D. Dresang (eds.) *What Government Does*. Beverly Hills: Sage.

Trivers, R. L. (1971) "The Evolution of Reciprocal Altruism." *Quarterly Review of Biology* 46:35-57.

Tursky, B., M. Lodge, M. Foley, R. Reeder and H. Foley. (1976) "Evaluation of the Cognitive Component of Political Issues by Use of Classical Conditioning." *Journal of Personality and Social Psychology* 34, 5:865-873.

Wahlke, J. and M. Lodge. (1972) "Psychophysiological Measures of Political Attitudes and Behavior." *Midwest Journal of Political Science* 4.

Welch, S. and A. Booth. "Crowding as a Factor in Political Aggression: Theoretical Aspects and an Analysis of Some Cross-National Data." *Social Science Information* 13, 4/5:151-162.

West, L. et al. (1969) "Sanity in the Sierra Madre: The Tarahumara Indians." Paper presented to the annual meeting of the American Psychiatric Association, May.

White, E. (1972) "Genetic Diversity and Political Life: Toward a Populational-Interaction Paradigm." *Journal of Politics* 34: 1203-1242.

Wiegele, T. C. (1971) "Toward a Psychophysiological Variable in Conflict Theory." *Experimental Study of Politics* 1, 2, July: 51-81.

Willhoite, F. Jr. (1976) "Primates and Political Authority: A Biobehavioral Perspective." *American Political Science Review* 70, December:1110-1126.

# 4
# Biopolitics and Political Elites

The previous chapter explored how a biopolitical perspective might contribute a more human understanding of mass political behavior within the larger political system. Shifting from macro-level concerns to the micro-level, we now want to examine how biological variables influence and temper the behavior of individuals in authoritative governmental roles. It is here at the individual level that knowledge from the life sciences will have its greatest impact on our understanding of how political elites, as human beings, function in decision-making situations. This is because studies can be operationalized with more facility and, in certain circumstances, will lend themselves to an experimental orientation. Furthermore, generalizations about individual behavior can remain at the individual level; there is no need to project those generalizations to higher levels with the familiar concomitant tenuousness. In addition it is at this level that the interdisciplinary nature of biopolitics will be felt most strongly, given the major and direct contributions from medicine (including psychosomatic medicine) and psychophysiology.

This chapter will examine the use of ethological methods to study elites, and then look at birth order, handedness, and self-perceptions of political leaders. A major concern will be a discussion of elites and the stresses of office in a biopolitical context. Following this, the chapter will explore a biosocial model of political charisma. Because elites pose special problems of inaccessibility for the political researcher, we will look at how a biopolitical perspective leads quite naturally to a range of remote assessment methodologies that can be used to extend our knowledge of elite behavior.

### Ethological Aspects of Elite Behaviors

Because a basic interest of political science lies in an understanding of the "authoritative allocation of values," political researchers quite naturally have had a primary interest in the holders of public power. It is these elites who occupy the roles that confer authority to act on behalf of the polity. Analysts who attempt to study elite behavior, however, are frequently confronted by two problems. First, while many elites, especially at the local level, are quite accessible, those at the national level frequently are not. And second, as an adjunct to this problem, students of political behavior have yet to develop satisfactory methods for studying elites remotely. Both of these problems are understandably troublesome to researchers because they would prefer to work in a milieu in which they have continuous and open communicative contact with the subjects of their investigations.

Interestingly, such a situation has long confronted ethologists who study animal behavior in an evolutionary context. These scholars also attempt to examine the behavior of subjects with whom they cannot verbally communicate or maintain full-time contact. Barner-Barry and Masters are political scientists who have utilized ethological methods and perspectives in their studies of authority and elite behavior.

Barner-Barry (1977) has been concerned that the study of authority has too narrowly focused on role-holders in government; and that if one is interested in a more basic knowledge of the nature of human authority as political scientists ought to be, then one must study authority and socialization to authority at a primary level. A knowledge of how authority manifests itself among small children and how nonauthoritative individuals respond to authoritative peers could provide not only the beginnings of a basic knowledge about authority, but also insights regarding the possible origins of human politics.

On the assumption that what people do is as important as what they say, Barner-Barry (1977:420) elected to study thirty-eight preschool children in the more naturalistic setting of a playgroup rather than in an experimental situation. She chose to focus on the 3½ to 6½ age group not only because such young children are less likely to be conscious of the researcher's presence, but also because "it seemed that if children would exhibit politically relevant behavior patterns, very young children would manifest these in basic form" (Barner-Barry, 1977:422). Data were gathered by nonparticipant observation, a technique that in large measure has grown out of previous ethological studies of the social behavior of non-human primates.

A further technique borrowed from ethology that Barner-Barry (1977:423) employed was that of event sampling. Rather than try to ascertain and code all behaviors within a certain time period, she sampled the continuum of events by extracting only those of a certain type, i.e. asymmetric interactions between two or more children in which an adult was absent. While this procedure ignores the richness of the behavioral repertoire of the subjects, it has the clear advantage of analytically extracting a particular type of event so that generalizations can be made regarding its attributes.

Asymmetric authority interactions among children included selection of types of play, leadership in play, articulation of rules, enforcement of rules, conflict resolution, etc. Based upon these interactions, three groups of children emerged: those who exercised these interaction roles most of the time, those who assumed them some of the time, and those who almost never exercised them. Barner-Barry described the first group as authoritative and the second and third as acquiescent.

In the playgroup under examination, three clearly authoritative children emerged on the basis of frequency counts of successful attempts to exercise authoritative behavior. The first of these was an essentially physical boy who used "force or the threat of force to control or direct the actions of another child;" but he would then "immediately make a special effort to placate and win over the [target] child" (Barner-Barry, 1977:431). A second child, a girl, exercised authoritative behavior almost exclusively on a verbal level. Intelligent, self-assured, and almost charismatic, she immediately became the center of attention of any group she joined. A third authoritative child fell somewhere between the first two. A boy, he was less inclined to use force than the first child and not nearly as verbal as the second child. He was a loner by choice, and willingly questioned adult authority. This child, as Barner-Barry (1977:432) indicates, "did not usually seek or create situations in which he might exercise authority, [but] neither did he hesitate to exercise authority when the opportunity presented itself." Interestingly, this last child produced the highest absolute number of successful attempts at authoritative behavior.

Several observations can be made about authoritative children in playgroup situations. When adults are absent, the authoritative children will easily assume authoritative roles for the group for the purposes of interpreting and enforcing the rules. In regard to the resolution of conflicts, again when adults were not present, children either fought their battle to the bitter end, or the combatants themselves halted the controversy. Authoritative children intervened in conflict situations by exhibiting threat displays in much the same way that such displays occur in the animal world. In almost all cases, nurturing behavior such as aid and protection was afforded by only the authoritative children.

Clearly, Barner-Barry has not provided an exhaustive examination of the nature of political authority. But she has attempted through the observational methods of ethology to push the study of authority back to a more fundamental level. Knowledge gained from her work with authoritative children might be subjected to replication in other contexts with both children and adults. We can agree with her when she states that "if some concept of authority is to be used, or even considered, as the basis for political inquiry, then there is much to be learned about the origins, development, and characteristics of those behavior patterns that constitute the building blocks of authority relationships" (Barner-Barry, 1977:442). Since much of the discipline of political science focuses on questions regarding the exercise of authority and socialization to authority, we should be eager to build an organized body of knowlege about authority that begins by examining the manner in which young people first come into contact with authority-guided and/or influenced situations.

A concept closely related to authority is that of attention structure. This conceptualization, developed by Chance (1967) while studying rank orders among primates, relates to the attention paid by an animal to those in higher rank. The pattern of attention, or attention structure, appears to be a critical mechanism relating to the understanding of behavior among primate groups. Barner-Barry (1978) and Masters (1978) have utilized the notion of attention in order to understand certain aspects of human political behavior.

Before looking at these applications of attention structure, however, let us briefly examine the meaning of this concept. Chance has apparently demonstrated that the individual social fields of primates can be conceptualized in terms of two forms of attention:

> Social groups cohere by distinct mechanisms of social attention. . . . One, the agonic [i.e. conflictful or struggling] is persistently cohesive, rigid in that it binds attention onto a centrally placed member of the group, involvement with whom is avoided by individuals maintaining the usually constant spatial separation. This state is supported by a persistent elevation of nervous arousal as a basis for a readiness for instant action. It is, therefore, coercive. The other, the hedonic, provides a fluctuating social cohesion, periodically reinstated by mutual display focused around the most flamboyant displayer. Individuals come together and often maintain long periods of body contact between dispersals, and so arousal is kept low. Hence, attention in the hedonic mode is capable of being distributed between the social and the non-social environment (Chance, 1977:3 quoted in Masters, 1978;4-5).

"In non-human primates," as Barner-Barry (1978:7) has indicated, "attention mainly takes the form of visual awareness. Members of a group, either by scanning, by glances or by body orientation, constantly keep informed on the location of the focal animal or animals." However, it should be mentioned that while Chance holds that attention is central to the structuring of social relationships within primate animal groups, Wilson (1975:517) has indicated that other factors such as "age structure, group size, and signal transmission rates" can also strongly influence social organization. Nevertheless, attention clearly is a significant element.

As examples of possible agonic and hedonic attention structures in human groups, Masters (1978:5) suggests two examples. A military commander engaging in a formal inspection of his troops could be looked upon as agonic; while patrons in a discotheque who have ceased dancing to observe a particularly capable dancer might be viewed as a form of hedonic attention. For the most part, agonic attention structures are held together by the fear of punishment, while hedonic structures anticipate reward.

As mentioned above, human ethologists have focused their studies on young children. In these efforts, attention is operationalized by determining who is looking at whom and with what frequency (Barner-Barry, 1978:12). Overall, the findings of this research point to the existence of attention structures in stable groups of young children quite similar to those found in certain types of nonhuman primate groups.

How might this knowledge of attention structure developed by ethologists be applied to elite political behavior? In a fascinating study, Masters (1978) conceives a presidential primary campaign as an attention device in which candidates attempt to structure public attention on themselves. Masters (1978:9-10) cites Theodore White's description of the appearance of Democratic presidential candidates at Serb Hall in Milwaukee during the 1972 primary:

> All the major candidates were scheduled for a drop-by on Saturday before election, and, by accident, four of them arrived at once—Humphrey, Lindsay, Muskie and McGovern. One caught again that strange, impossible-to-describe political

moment of mood and portent: John Lindsay, blond, tall, selfpossessed, wandering the tables with no attention, interrupting the muscular working men and their wives in housedresses, as they ate, to shake hands and introduce himself. The Secret Service had already decided that Lindsay was not a serious candidate and so the six-foot-three Lindsay, stripped of the one dubious official badge of candidacy, must stroll the strange tables accompanied only by his devoted five-foot-eight New York police detective, Pat Vecchio. Then, Muskie, arriving late—his large frame stooped, his head down, swathed in a melancholy he could not shake, to be ignored. And Humphrey, at table with a posse of recognizable Wisconsin ethnics, munching away at his fish with gusto, attended by cameras, TV lights and newsmen—until the moment of McGovern's arrival, when the magnetism passed, as if a conductor had pointed with his baton to the real candidate. Cameras, lights, newsmen had moved, click, by unspoken command, to bunch around the Senator from South Dakota, and fallen into the serpentine formation which, in any contemporary political jostle, marks the path that the star cuts through the crowd (sic.) (White, 1973: 106).

Clearly, this gathering could have been described easily by attention structure theory; and a careful post-hoc analysis of films of the event might have been able to quantify the amount of visual contact accorded candidates by those in attendance. It is interesting that the final results of this election showed McGovern winning with 30 percent of the vote; Humphrey had 21 percent, and Muskie captured only 10 percent. Lindsay finished last in a field of six and subsequently withdrew from national contention. Thus, Masters (1978:12) observes that "political campaigns in contemporary democracy can be seen as an attempt, on the part of actual or potential leaders, to impose a 'centric' [i.e. focused on a specific individual] attention structure on publics who might otherwise continue to follow 'acentric' patterns of behavior." This comment hints at numerous theoretical and operational issues in an attention structure research orientation that need not be discussed here, but that ultimately would be important in this type of study.

A second effort by Barner-Barry (1978) built upon her previous work. Again utilizing nonparticipant observation combined with event sampling, she studied asymetric dyadic interaction between young children in which one child exercised "more influence over the development and/or outcome of the interactions" than did the other child. The purpose of the study was to begin to develop knowledge about the roots of human political authority. Barner-Barry (1978: 25-26) found that consistent with the literature on nonhuman primate social systems, human systems of social regulation (as seen in her sample of children) are not based exclusively on brute power or force. Additional elements of skill, merit, and personal attractiveness also appear to be important components:

> Thus, it would seem that the child who is at the center of attention and who exercises *de facto* authority is the focal child because s/he is the most interesting and seemingly competent person around at that particular time and in that particular place. To some extent, the focal child seems to be one who most successfully exploits the complexity of which the human organism is capable at a given age and in given circumstances in somewhat the same way that, perhaps, the focal nonhuman primate is the one who most successfully exploits the relevant potentials of that species (1978:26).

However, Barner-Barry (1978:26) emphasizes that "this is not to suggest that humans do the same things as nonhuman primates, but rather that we do similar things which seem to serve the same function. That function is the giving of organization, form, and predictibility to one aspect of the social environment—the regulation of governing of relatively stable social units."

Central to Barner-Barry's (1978:26) writings is the perspective of the human ethologists who "demonstrate the value of thinking about human beings in terms of a basic biological, primate model." Such a model exerts "a valuable discipline on our natural wish to see oursleves as unique," but it also underscores "our acute awareness of the complexity of human behavior."

These observations are particularly relevant in studying the nature of political authority and the manner in which elites exercise that authority. If an ethological framework yields a comparative dimension to our attempt to explore the roots of elite political behavior, then we should not be fearful of exploiting such an orientation even though it will require the development of imaginative research designs when applied to real political situations.

## Birth Order, Handedness, and Energy Levels in Elites

In turning away from some of the larger issues suggested by the field of ethology, let us examine several specific findings regarding birth order, handedness, and energy levels in elites. All of these factors have been the subject of some scholarly interest, perhaps more as background information to provide insights into the political personality rather than as powerful predictors of behavior.

The literature on birth order, particularly in the discipline of psychology, has been fairly extensive. It suggests that first born children are significantly overrepresented among the socially visible, the scientific and academic elite, and among college students and Rhodes scholars (Altus, 1966, Warren, 1966, Renshon, 1975, and Stewart, 1977). Of particular interest to political scientists is the fact that firstborns and only children have been found to have a higher need achievement coupled with a strong ability to be successful in academic pursuits. Because of this, Forbes (1971) reasoned that firstborns would have a greater tendency to enter the elective political arena as well as be more successful in that endeavor than later born children. In order to test these hypotheses, he surveyed all candidates for contested seats in the 1970 Illinois legislative elections. The findings were curious. Because of high need achievement, one would have expected an overrepresentation of firstborns among the pool of candidates. This was not borne out, and Forbes (1971:1242) comments that "the failure to find an overrepresentation of firstborns is one of only a few such failures reported in the literature." Apparently, being a firstborn is not a recruitment factor for *entrance* into the political arena. However, once in the electoral contest, firstborns were more likely to win than middleborns, but so too were lastborns more likely to win than middleborns. "This indicates," says Forbes (1971:1242), "that while firstborns or lastborns are not overrepresented among political candidates, they are overrepresented among successful candidates." Forbes reflects that personality factors associated with the firstborn and the lastborn must be operative during the political campaign to account for the significant successes of those two groups over the middleborns.

Even though Forbes's sample was fairly large (128 candidate respondents), his work focused on only one election campaign. Such work could easily be replicated in numerous past or future campaigns both in the United States and in other countries. If further work does demonstrate that birth order factors bear a different relationship to political activity than they do to other types of social behavior, then perhaps we will have uncovered a modest tool to assist in the prediction or understanding of electoral success.

Another factor related to birth order as a "soft" measure of elite assessment is handedness, normally defined as an individual's preference for one hand over the other for such tasks as writing. Biological factors appear to be involved in the selection of handedness because all human societies have overwhelming majorities of right-handed members. Left-handedness is clearly a minority phenomenon comprising normally only 9 to 12 percent of a population but occasionally rising to 30 percent. Cultural pressures encouraging right-handedness and many social taboos associated with left-handedness are also in evidence in both ancient and modern societies. In a series of publications, LaPonce (1972, 1976, an 1978) has focused on questions of personal directionality as it relates to politics. He (1976:46-47) has pointed out that very early in its life a child is ambidexterous, but that sometime between the second and the fourth year a preference, which is most often right-handed, emerges. "This evolution from ambidexterity to right-handedness is also used to support the theory that hand unbalance is linked to brain unbalance and that right hand dominance is linked to the development of speech, a faculty primarily located in the left hemisphere of the brain, the hemisphere that controls the movements of the right hand." Moreover, "the latter interpretation, that which fits best the data available, distinguishes man from other animals both by speech and right-handedness, two characteristics linked to brain hemisphere specialization." Is the fact of hand preference, LaPonce has asked, of any use in political analysis? He attempted to answer this question in the affirmative.

Reasoning that left-handers view themselves as awkwardly placed in a right-handed world, LaPonce (1976:51) argued that "we should expect . . . that, on the average, the left-hander would be at a constant disadvantage, a disadvantage leading him to be relatively dissatisfied with the present and hopeful of a more equalitarian future." In terms of psychological orientation LaPonce hypothesized that the left-hander might have a mind set roughly equivalent to that of members of minorities in relation to the dominant groups within a society. Since disadvantaged minorities are frequently change-oriented in terms of elevating their position within a society, and since left-wing politics is normally associated with change, is it possible that biological left-handedness is related to political leftism? LaPonce is aware that he could be charged with offering an absurd hypothesis based on a "fortuitous semantic similarity," but his reasoning (above) linking left-handedness with a desire for change seems a priori to be sound.

Based upon this presumed linkage, LaPonce (1976) set out to test whether social, psychological, or political characteristics might be correlated with left-handedness. Overall, the results were not strong, but a modest correlation was found in the political dimension. Working in the Canadian political context, LaPonce (1976:53) found more left-handers than right-handers preferred the political left defined as embracing both the Liberal party and the Socialist party. In general, however, few behavioral correlates of left-handedness were found; and the study was declared by its author to be inconclusive.

Nevertheless, LaPonce has opened a line of political inquiry that might have direct relevance to the study of elites. We can easily determine, after all, the hand preference of at least central elites. If a stronger literature develops linking handedness, brainsidedness, and personality and/or behavioral characteristics of individuals, it might prove fruitful to conduct studies that will more narrowly focus on the personal characteristics of political elites.

Given the well-known observation that politics is an occupation demanding an enormous and continuous expenditure of personal energy on the part of elite actors, particularly at the highest levels of government, it is somewhat surprising, as Schwartz (1970) indicates, that so little analytic attention has been paid to the study of energy levels. To Schwartz, personal energy is an important intervening variable between attitudinal predispositions or personality and the behavior of an individual actor. In order to test this linkage Schwartz (1970:11) hypothesized "that people who perceive themselves as comparatively high in energy level would tend significantly to adopt active behavioral orientations to politics; . . . whereas the perception of self as relatively low in energy level should be significantly associated with more passive forms of political orientation." (A similar study linking body images with basic political orientations is reported in Schwartz et al., 1975.) For this study active behavior orientations consisted of postures such as nonconformity, reformism, and revolutionism, while the more passive orientations were described as conformity and ritualism.

This was a survey study in which the sample consisted of university students and faculty members. Energy levels were assessed by asking subjects to respond to two items: "I think of myself as being low in energy. I'm often physically listless, or tired or run down;" and "I get tired faster than most people." Responses to these items were correlated with questions designed to tap the active and passive behavioral political orientations listed above.

The findings of this study, though tentative and weak, were in the predicted direction. "The perception of personal energy level does have significant impacts . . . on the selection of a basic behavioral response tendency toward politics" (Schwartz,

1970:15). For example, individuals who perceived themselves as high in personal energy also indicated that behaviorally they were less conformist, more reform minded. However, these individuals did not react in the predicted direction regarding attitudes toward revolution and violence.

This study is of interest in several respects. Schwartz's desire to demonstrate associations between individuals' perception of their own physical health and willingness to adopt certain behaviors toward the political system is imaginative. His hypotheses are certainly consistent with the observations in Chapter 3 regarding nutritional status and sedentary life-style which may contribute to general levels of health. Nevertheless, there appear to be some fundamental methodological issues at stake in attempting to assess health status through traditional survey research methods exclusively. As is well known in the medical profession, self-assessment of health status is a highly risky procedure for acquiring data. Patient self-assessments are routinely checked with harder measures of biological pro-cessess.

As an example of the danger of self-assessments of health status—and a paper-and-pencil survey instrument assumes that a subject can make an accurate assessment—a study, by Wiegele, Plowman, and Catey (1975) can be cited. We asked a group of fifty college-student subjects to rate their health as either excellent, good, fair, or poor. Fifty-eight percent rated themselves as excellent, 42 percent as good. No subjects judged themselves to be in fair or poor health. Moreover, 60 percent said they exercised strenuously an hour or more per day, 12 percent got a half-hour or more per day, and only 28 percent labelled themselves as engaging in very little or no exercise. Treadmill testing is recognized as providing an excellent assessment of cardiorespiratory fitness, and therefore is a good test of overall health. When we put our subjects on the treadmill, only 12 percent scored in the average, good, and excellent categories *combined*. Thus, though 100 percent of our subjects described themselves as in good or excellent health, a much more objective measure, the treadmill, revealed that only 12 percent could be described by those labels.

Furthermore, individuals who get an hour or more of strenuous exercise per day should score very well in treadmill testing. Because these results were not forthcoming, we suspected that since exercise is socially acceptable and a sign of good health, our subjects told us in their survey answers what they thought we wanted to hear. Thus, though Schwartz is correct to suspect that health might be related to political behavior, it is also true that if political scientists are going to utilize health variables, they will have to develop a repertoire of harder measures of health status. Certainly, the paper-and-pencil survey provides an unacceptable substitute.

## Elites and the Stresses of Public Office

One of the major themes of this book is that political analysts have failed to take into account the realities of political life *at the level at which it is lived.* At this level, biological considerations interact with emotional, rational, and psychological factors within a real human being. For the student of biopolitics, it is not simply observed political behavior such as a state of the union address or voting activity on a legislative floor that is of interest; it is also the changes within and responses of the individual *as a human person* that merit attention. It is here at the confluence of public role responsibilities and private, internal behavioral and physiological adaptations that we will ultimately gain our most precise and insightful understandings of how elite human beings as individuals react to the experience of public life. To seek this kind of dual information is, of course, difficult. But once we achieve a body of knowledge and meaningful correlations between internal processes and "external" behavior, we will begin to approach a basic understanding of the totality of elite political life.

"Role overload," a concept with special reference to the stresses of public office, refers to "a condition in which the individual is faced with a set of obligations which, *taken as a set*, requires him to do more than he is able in the time available. In cases under this rubric, each separate demand is within the capabilities of the focal person; however, the set of demands is beyond these capabilities because of some limitation upon the time available for performance" (Sales, 1969:325-326). Political elites, especially at the national level, often find themselves in a situation that can only be described as an overload of role responsibilities. In this regard, says Sales (1969:326), "role overload cannot be considered either a function of the person or a characteristic of his environment; rather, it relates to the *interaction* between the person and the environment."

It is conceivable that political elites seek out roles that encourage an overload of responsibility because this might be perceived as enhancing political power. Furthermore, certain kinds of personalities appear to be peculiarly disposed to role overload. In searching for behavioral correlates of coronary heart disease, Jenkins, Rosenman, and Friedman (1967) identified two now classic personality types.

> Type A . . . is characterized primarily by excessive drive, aggressiveness, ambition, involvement in competitive activities, frequent vocational deadlines, pressure for vocational productivity, [and] an enhanced sense of time urgency. . . . The converse . . . pattern, called Type B, is characterized by the relative absence of this interplay of psychological traits and situational pressures. The Type B subject is more relaxed and more easy going, seldom becomes impatient and takes more time to enjoy avocational pursuits. He is not easily irritated and works steadily, but without a feeling of being driven by a lack of time. He is not preoccupied with social achievement, and is less competitive in his occupational and avocational pursuits (Jenkins et al., 1967:371, quoted in Sales, 1979:329).

The drive, aggressiveness, and ambition of the Type A personality appears to be consistent with political elites who occupy role overloaded positions. Thus, political recruitment might very well select for Type A individuals. At the same time, such recruitment might predispose those individuals not only to increased risks of coronary heart disease but also to a range of maladies related to attempts to cope with increasing levels of psychological stress.

In contemporary societies one method of coping with the stresses of role overload is through the use of chemical tranquilizers. Two common tranquilizers, librium and chlorpromazine, may produce a general lessening of emotional sensitivity. Jaros (1972:7) has written that chlorpromazine can prevent a person from effectively monitoring sensory feedback from his own behavior. Among decision makers this could lead to a situation in which only gross alternatives are perceived as viable.

For obvious reasons we do not have a good data base on nonalcoholic drug abuse among elites. Occasionally, however, items of information do become available that indicate that elites are not immune from acts of poor judgment in regard to their own persons. Halberstam (1972) recounts an anecdote in which British Prime Minister Anthony Eden revealed that he was "living on benzedrine" just prior to the Suez Crisis. Benzedrine distorts one's judgment by artifically inducing feelings of omnipotence and energy. As a victim of Addison's disease, President John F. Kennedy may have experienced the symptoms of irritability, depression, emotional instability, and negativistic outlook. Cortisone, which Kennedy ingested for treatment, produces the frequent behavioral effect of not only reversing the irritability, depression, and instability of Addison's disease, but also resulting in side effects characterized by euphoric outlook and excessive affability. Moreover, L'Étang (1970:189) points out that elite patients have a tendency to ignore and even conceal the side effects of drugs.

With the heavy responsibilities of public office, it should not be surprising that most national capitals might be characterized as having a high stress social environment. Alcoholic drug abuse in these situations is common. For example, Washington D.C. has a per capita rate of alcohol consumption that is more than double the national average. While drinking problems such as those encountered by former Representative Wilbur Mills make humorous newspaper copy, situations that become public no doubt represent only the tip of a large iceberg. Indeed, the National Clearinghouse for Alcohol Information indicated that a study of alcoholism among high-ranking U.S. government officials had been deemed necessary; but for reasons of sensitivity it was not undertaken.

Associated with the demands of office are dangers to an official's personal and family life. The long hours spent away from one's spouse and children can create stresses within a family and/or marriage that can influence political performance. Foreman (1977) reports that even though President Carter early in his administration sent a memorandum to his immediate staff stating that "all of you will be more valuable to me and the country with rest and a stable home life," staff members reported that they routinely worked twelve to fourteen hours per day, seven days a week. It is by no means clear whether an individual who is subjected to such a grueling work situation is submitting because of personal loyalty, sense of national purpose, or personal behavioral idiosyncracies and/or objectives.

In the next chapter we will deal at length with the topic of voice stress analysis as an unobtrusive measure of elite stress in international crisis situations. Suffice it to say here that it appears possible to electronically analyze the human voice in order to determine issues, ideas, themes and personal considerations that are causing psychological discomfort to a speaker. While it is often assumed that the motivation of leaders revolves around political considerations, this assumption is based upon observed behavior. Analysts usually infer motivations from a printed text of a speech, statement, or press conference. But if we are to take Schubert seriously, we ought to check our observations with some type of monitoring of internal physiological processes. It is in this task that voice stress analysis is particularly helpful.

In order to test whether there might be a difference between the manifest meanings of the spoken word and the underlying physiological arousal that occurs while speaking, we subjected to voice stress analysis two extemporaneous speeches of former president Richard M. Nixon (Wiegele, 1978). The 1962 California gubernatorial concession and the 1974 farewell to his staff were selected because both efforts were delivered at

known stress points in Nixon's life: the loss of the governor-
ship in 1962 seemed to indicate that his political life had come
to a premature end, and the forced 1974 departure from the
presidency marked perhaps the greatest scandal in American
political history. A traditional analysis of these speeches would
have focused on the political subject matter contained in them.
But voice stress analysis appears to have penetrated beyond the
surface meanings of words and into the changing levels of
physiological arousal in Nixon while he spoke. For example,
we found that it was not the political themes that caused the
most stress or discomfort in Nixon; rather, it was the intensely
personal themes that bothered him the most. Concern for
himself as a defeated man, the nature of human tragedy, and
reflections on his parents caused more discomfort in Nixon
than any of the political issues about which he also spoke.
Indeed, events that are traditionally viewed by the electorate as
political failures were perceived by Nixon as serious *personal*
failures. Further work using voice stress analysis might be able
to demonstrate that other leaders in similar situations may
view their political fortunes in highly personal terms. It might
be worthwhile to add that decisional choices designed to restore
personal worth or prestige could be fundamentally different
from those directed at the precise resolution of a political
problem. Indeed, the ability to probe psychophysiologically
the consciousness of elites might provide for analysts a new
conception of leadership as seen through the evidences of stress
in their voices.

Reflections on stress by political elites have been common in
memoirs and interviews. In Wiegele (1977) we combed
approximately forty volumes of memoirs of American presidents and other high level decision makers for references to
stress-inducing occurrences. It was clear from this work that
elites were far more sensitive to what was going on "inside"
themselves than they would have admitted publicly while in
office. One of our interesting findings was that self-perceptions
regarding one's high level of authority are frequently negative
For example, Woodrow Wilson was viewed by his wife as a
"splendid Bengal tiger I had once seen—never still, moving,

restless, resentful of his bars" (Wilson, 1938:67). Lyndon Johnson "felt a strong desire to go back to Texas while there was still time—time to enjoy life with my wife and my daughters, to work in earnest at being a rancher on the land I loved, to slow down, to reflect, to live" (Johnson, 1971:93). President Truman shared these feelings about the pressures of public office: "someday the nightmare will be over and maybe we can all go back to normal living" (Truman, 1973). Shortly after leaving office, Henry A. Kissinger alluded to the problems of stress and role overload: "When you are Secretary of State, you have to deal with probably more problems than can be handled in any one day; and you have the constant sense that you are responsible for what may happen six months to a year down the road. . . . It is both exhilarating and creates great pressures" (Weinraub, 1977:47).

The popular press has frequently raised the question of whether female leaders might be able to tolerate the stresses of high level decision making as well as male leaders presumably handle them. Unfortunately, this question has been subjected to considerably more speculation than serious research. In biopolitical work, only one study has been undertaken in an attempt to associate biological variables in females, in this case the menstrual cycle, with political attitudes and behavior. Peterson (n.d.) advanced several hypotheses linking menstrual discomfort with political and attitudinal variables such as participation in the political process (voting) and attitudes toward system support or non-support. This study attempted to demonstrate that degree of menstrual discomfort would predict certain political attitudes and behaviors. While most of the correlations, as Peterson indicates, reached a minimal level of statistical significance and were in the predicted directions, nevertheless the results were disappointing. At best, the correlations might be described as "suggestive relationships." Even more confounding was the fact that the menstrual distress indices correlated inconsistently with differing political attitudes.

Peterson (n.d.) carefully described two problems associated with his effort. First, "the biological (or physiological) effects of the cycle are confounded by and interwoven with psychological effects and cultural expectations (often the result of the socialization process)." These effects were difficult to disentangle with precision. Related to this difficulty was a second which is quite important: menstrual distress was self-reported by using paper-and-pencil questionnaires. Not only did cultural factors and psychological perceptions condition responses, but, as we indicated in discussing Schwartz's work on energy levels above, self-reporting of biological variables is highly risky. As Peterson correctly concludes, "if a researcher wish[es] to discern the impact (if any) of the physiology of sex on behavior, . . . more direct and valid measures [must] be developed and used." It is conceivable that if true biological measures had been employed in this study, the results might have been different. With larger numbers of females assuming elite political roles, the stimulus for such work might become greater in the future.

## A Biosocial Model of Charisma

Students of elite political behavior have had a continuing interest in the study of charisma and charismatic leadership. But Hummel (1970:2) has complained that while social scientists have carefully described charismatic behavior, they have so far failed to explain it. As a result, he attempts to lay out a research strategy that incorporates a strong orientation to the life sciences and that might be utilized to explain charismatic phenomena.

Weber has defined charisma as "a quality of a person which passes for something outside of the everyday, . . . and because of which that person is appraised as equipped with powers or peculiarities that are not accessible to [just] any other person and are supernatural or superhuman or at least specifically outside the everyday,. or . . . as divinely dispatched or as exemplary and therefore as "leader" (quoted in Hummel, 1970:6). While accepting the basic thrust of this definition, Hummel argues that it is an incomplete definition because it ignores new information from the contemporary life sciences.

Leaning heavily on Gehlen (1950), Hummel reasons that human beings have both an inner life and an external life. Their inner and biological needs require satisfaction that is not preprogrammed in any set of drives or schema of interaction. Rather, they attempt to construct an external or social reality that is compatible with their inner lives and with their biological nature. When social reality undergoes significant alteration, such changes "threaten the previously socialized individual's very existence—both in a psychological and biological way for the reasons of interconnection between World, psyche, and organism" (Hummel, 1970:30). This can create a social crisis which Hummel designates the "precharismatic crisis."

The precharismatic social crisis that prepares the ground for the emergence of a charismatic leader "is the result of breaks in established routines, especially of routines toward which orientation was established early in life in primary social- ization and of routines that fulfill fundamental biological needs" (Hummel, 1970:41). Furthermore, Hummel hypoth- esizes that an overload of stimuli from the social environment causes the precharismatic crisis. This overload has its impact on the cortical centers of the brain thereby preventing an effective integration of responses to incoming stimuli. Hummel's consideration of brain activity with regard to the precharismatic crisis is similar to Davies's discussion in Chapter 3 of brain disturbances during periods of revolution- ary upheaval.

Critical to Hummel's (1970:55) reasoning is that "the establishment of the charismatic follower-leader relationship may be an expression of renewed primary bonding tendencies which are biologically based." Bonding, then—a concept borrowed from ethology—appears to be at the core of citizen attachments to charismatic leaders, which in turn give leaders immense power over their followers. Hummel (1970:56) suggests, therefore, that charismatic bonding may constitute a form of response to social stress.

A biosocial model of charisma contributes to a substantial extension of theory regarding the nature of the charismatic phenomenon. The precharismatic crisis appears to have features that are strikingly similar to those giving rise to collective aggression. If Hummel's concepts can be operationalized and if his propositions can be tested, we will have taken a significant step toward combining powerful information from both the life and social sciences regarding one of the most intriguing of phenomena in political life. If such work is pursued, new understandings of the nature of leadership and elite behavior are sure to emerge.

## The Remote Assessment of Elites

As we mentioned in the opening remarks for this chapter, the study of political elites has been a major arena of inquiry for political analysts. Nevertheless, those who have worked in this area, particularly at the national level, are quick to point out that access to critical components of information about elites is frequently difficult, if not impossible, to bring about. Personal idiosyncracies are carefully guarded. Medical records are seldom made public, especially if they provide clues to mental health status. Understandably, the professional ethics of physicians prevents them from releasing information that might be of great value to a political researcher. Leaders themselves are generally disinclined to provide, for obvious political reasons, information about their physical health or psychological state. Because of this situation, we have normally relied on "soft" assessments of elite personalities combined with a good deal of deductive reasoning and intuition. These might be described as peripheral measures of the elite person, peripheral in the sense that they do not constitute the direct measurement of the individual human being.

The idea of signal leakage might provide the conceptual framework into which a number of "hard" indices of remote assessment could be fit (Wiegele, forthcoming). Eckman and Friesen (1975:144) defined signal leakage as "the nonintended betrayal of a feeling the person is trying to conceal." To these scholars, the "neuro-anatomy and cultural influences combine to produce specific types of body movements and facial expressions which escape efforts to deceive and emerge as leakage." Indeed, certain parts of the body have specific sending capacities that can be indexed by the length of time needed to transmit the information, by the "number of discriminable stimulus patterns which can be emitted," and by visibility or the degree to which the analyst is able to observe the leakage content (Eckman and Friesen, 1969:93-94). For the political analyst, signal leakage might be more broadly defined as the nonintended verbal or nonverbal emission of a measurable clue to psychological state by an individual human being. It should be pointed out, however, that elites can quite intentionally leak signals regarding their psychological states in the normal course of their public communications. In the present discussion, we are excluding such intentional leakage. Without providing an exhaustive list, some examples of signal leakage that would be useful in the study of elites can be provided.

Frank (1973:27) has developed a theory of verbal kinesics which holds that "certain semantic forms, including spacial symbols and referential distantiation, universally appear in verbal discourse." These forms "represent psycholinguistic tools by which body-environment and body-behavioral responses can be actualized"; and such forms index "underlying psychological states and are isomorphic with parallel behavioral dispositions." Signal leakage occurs in Frank's theoretical formulations because the use of symbols is not topic bound; and a message beyond the manifest meaning of words is leaked to the skilled analyst. In order to test the theory of verbal kinesics, Frank performed content analyses on thirty-eight state of the union messages of U.S. presidents during a thirty-five year period. He found that "spatial symbol patterns do shift, with statistical significance, internal to [individual] speeches according to the degree of perceived topic-stress on the part of the speech giver" (Frank, 1973:35). In a subsequent effort, Frank (1977) combined speech disturbance measures with three nonverbal indicators of leakage: eyeblinks, gross bodily movements, and nods. These nonverbal indicators indexed negative affect and passive responses to stressful situations. Frank (1977:79) concluded that his multiple indicator "techniques can help to unearth new and fresh dimensions of actor-

behavior and orientation which would be otherwise unavail-
able were the researcher to concentrate solely upon an analysis
of the image that the subject is consciously trying to portray in
his particular sociopolitical role."

Utilizing an ethological perspective that employed nonverbal measures of the leakage of cues to index general arousal,
Schubert (forthcoming) studied the judges of the Swiss Federal
Tribunal who were engaged in the act of rendering decisions.
The nonverbal measures he utilized, listed in increasing order
of hypothesized arousal, were facial, capital, oral nonverbal,
manual, corporal, and ambulatory. Schubert found that
nonverbal communication "was an important component of
the social interaction observed to occur among small groups of
judges." Another interesting finding was that emotional
messages were most often communicated by nonverbal means.
On the basis of his research Schubert feels comfortable in
suggesting that nonverbal communication "can be used as an
indicator of arousal," and he implies that further work based
upon ethological models might be highly productive.

Another potential method of remote assessment of political
elites might be found in the study of pupillometry (Hess, 1965).
In this field the change in horizontal or vertical diameter of the
pupil from a previously established baseline measure is
normally the leaked signal. Janisse (1977:14) indicates,
however, that other pupil measures such as average size, peak
and minimum size, and variance have also been employed.
Equipment needed to gather data on the pupil includes, among
other devices, movie or television cameras and/or electronic
scanners. Pupillometry has been utilized to study a variety of
topics including attitudes, anxiety, drug abuse, personality,
and choice behavior.

One of the difficulties with this research is that it has made its
greatest progress in experimental as opposed to applied
settings. This is understandable because head movement
changes the orientation of a subject's eyes to a light source,
thereby influencing pupil dilation. In order to prevent these
random occurrences, head position must be held constant
which in turn has all but prevented applied research. Neverthe-

less, Janisse (1977:169) has pointed out that technical break-throughs are likely and that ultimately it might be possible to remotely assess the leakage of signs of fatigue and stress through pupil examination. Such a capability would be highly useful to a political researcher in the study of elites or in making real-time assessments during, for example, inter-national crises.

Scholars in the field of speech communication have developed analytical techniques based upon disturbances in extemporaneous speech. These disturbances can be concep-tualized as leaked signals that give clues to psychological states such as anxiety. Mahl (1956), for example, developed several categories of speech disturbances: the use of "ah," sentence correction, sentence incompletion, repetition, stuttering, intruding, incoherent sound, tongue slips, and omissions. Intuitively, experienced journalists have inferred the existence of presidential fatigue from "verbal slip-ups." Smith (1977) reported several uncharacteristic speech disturbances or "flubs" made by Jimmy Carter during a press conference, and juxtaposed these with other observations about Carter's appearance, such as care in the combing of hair and appearance of the skin. This leakage led to a judgment of extreme fatigue that was later corroborated. Rigorous content-analytic routines might be developed to aid in generating and analyzing data based upon speech disturbances. This leakage of signals can be remotely assessed with ease from audio recordings.

## Conclusions

There are numerous biologically based research orientations that have been utilized to study the nature of authority and elite behavior. Such work has attempted to explore the origins of human dominance and submission patterns by employing methodologies from animal behavior studies. Further, we have examined some information from medicine and a range of stress-related studies to gain insights into the lives of political elites. Much of this work represents a preliminary groping with new ideas in an attempt to develop more accurate appraisals of elite behavior. Hopefully, this scholarship will continue and each thread of research will be intensified to the extent that in the future it might be possible to develop a retinue of measures that, when combined, will be able to provide powerful assessment routines. Such combinations should allow biopolitical analysts to provide accurate psychophysiological appraisals of political leaders. Once those appraisals are done with confidence, they might be comfortably linked with behavioral assessments. A biobehavioral knowledge of leaders might force us to revise our scholarship in this area in a fundamental way.

**References**

Altus, W. D. (1966) "Birth Order and Its Sequelae." *Science* 151: 44-49.

Barner-Barry, C. (1978) "The Biological Correlates of Power and Authority: Dominance and Attention Structure." Paper presented to the annual convention of the American Political Science Association, New York, August-September.

————. (1977) "An Observational Study of Authority in a Preschool Peer Group." *Political Methodology* 4:415-449.

Chance, M. R. A. (1977) "The Social Structure of Attention and the Operation of Intelligence." Paper presented to the 139th annual meeting of the British Association for the Advancement of Science, August-September.

————. (1967) "Attention Structure as the Basis of Primate Ranking Orders." *Man* 2:503-518.

Eckman, P. and W. V. Friesen. (1975) *Unmasking the Face: A Guide to Recognizing Emotions from Facial Clues.* Englewood Cliffs, N.J.: Prentice-Hall.

————. (1969) "Non-Verbal Leakage and Clues to Deception." *Psychiatry* 32, 1, February:88-105.

Forbes, G. B. (1971) "Birth Order and Political Success: A Study of the 1970 Illinois General Elections." *Psychological Reports* 29:1239-1242.

Foreman, L. (1977) "Spend More Time with the Family? Carter's Aides Find They Can't." *New York Times*, February 24, p. 30.

Frank, R. S. (1977) "Nonverbal and Paralinguistic Analysis of Political Behavior: The First McGovern-Humphrey California Primary Debate," in M. G. Hermann and T. W. Milburn, eds.

―――. (1973) *Linguistic Analysis of Political Elites: A Theory of Verbal Kinesics.* Beverly Hills: Sage.

Gehlen, A. (1950) *Der Mensch: seine natur und siene Stelling in der Welt.* Bonn: Athenaum Verlag.

Halberstam, M. (1972) "Who's Medically Fit for the White House?" *New York Times Magazine,* October 22.

Hermann, M. G. and T. W. Milburn, eds. (1977) *A Psychological Examination of Political Leaders.* New York: Free Press.

Hess, E. H. (1965) "Attitude and Pupil Size." *Scientific American* 212:46-54.

Hummel, R. P. (1970) "A Case for a Biosocial Model of Charisma." Paper presented to the Eighth Congress of the International Political Science Association, Munich, August 31–September 5.

Janisse, M. P. (1977) *Pupillometry: The Psychology of Pupillary Response.* Washington: Hemisphere Publishing Corp.

Jaros, D. (1972) "Biochemical Desocialization: Depressants and Political Behavior." *Midwest Journal of Political Science* 16, February:1-28.

Jenkins, C. D., R. H. Rosenman, and M. Friedman. (1967) "Development of an Objective Psychological Test for the Determination of the Coronary-Prone Behavior Pattern in Employed Men." *Journal of Chronic Diseases* 20:371-379.

Johnson, L. B. (1971) *The Vantage Point.* New York: Popular Library.

LaPonce. J. A. (1978) "Relating Biological, Physical, and Political Phenomena: The Case of Up and Down." *Social Science Information* 17, 3:385-397.

―――. (1976) "The Left-Hander and Politics," in A. Somit, ed.

―――. (1972) "In Search of the Stable Elements of the Left-Right Landscape." *Comparative Politics,* 4, 4, July:455-475.

L'Étang, H. (1970) *The Pathology of Leadership.* New York: Hawthorne.

Mahl, G. F. (1956) "Disturbances and Silences in the Patient's Speech in Psychotherapy." *Journal of Abnormal and Social Speech in Psychology* 53:1-15.

Masters, R. D. (1978) "Attention Structures and Political Campaigns." Paper presented to the annual convention of the American Political Science Association, New York, August-September.

Peterson, S. A. (n.d.) "The Menstrual Cycle and Politics: A Preliminary Exploration." Unpublished manuscript.

Renshon, S. A. (1975) "Birth Order and Political Socialization," in Schwartz, D. C. and S. K. Schwartz, eds., pp. 69-95.

Sales, S. M. (1969) "Organizational Role as a Risk Factor in Coronary Disease." *Administrative Science Quarterly*, September: 325-336.

Schubert, G. (forthcoming) "Nonverbal Communication as Political Behavior," in M. R. Key and D. Preziosi, eds., *Nonverbal Communication Today: Current Research* (1979).

Schwartz, D. C. (1970) "Perceptions of Personal Energy and the Adoption of Basic Behavioral Orientations to Politics." Paper presented to the Eighth Congress of the International Political Science Association, Munich.

Schwartz, D. C. and S. K. Schwartz, eds. (1975) *New Directions in Political Science*. New York: Free Press.

Schwartz, D. C., J. Garrison, and J. Alouf. (1975) "Health, Body Images, and Political Socialization," in Schwartz, D. C. and S. K. Schwartz, eds., pp. 96-126.

Smith, H. (1977) "A President Under Strain." *New York Times*, July 29, p. A9.

Somit, A., ed. (1976) *Biology and Politics*. Mouton: Paris.

Stewart, L. H. (1977) "Birth Order and Political Leadership," in M. G. Hermann, ed., pp. 206-236.

Truman, M. (1973) *Harry S. Truman*. New York: Morrow.

Warren, J. R. (1966) "Birth Order and Social Behavior." *Psychological Bulletin* 65:38-49.

Weinraub, B. (1977) "Kissinger Back in Academia as the Professor of Diplomacy." *New York Times*, March 10, pp. 35 and 47.

White, T. (1973) *Making of the President 1972*. New York: Atheneum.

Wiegele, T. C. (1979) "Signal Leakage and the Remote Psychological Assessment of Foreign Policy Elites," in L. Falkowski, ed., *Psychological Models in International Politics*. Boulder, Co.: Westview Press.

_____. (1978) "Physiologically-Based Content Analysis: An Application in Political Communication," in B. D. Ruben, ed.,

*Communication Yearbook 2.* New Brunswick, N.J.: Transaction Books.

―――. (1977) "Models of Stress and Disturbances in Elite Political Behaviors: Psychological Variables and Political Decision Making," in R. S. Robins, ed., *Psychopathology and Political Leadership.* New Orleans: Tulane Studies in Political Science, pp. 79-111.

Wiegele, T. C. , S. A. Plowman, and R. Catey. (1975) "Cardiorespiratory Health and Dimensions of Subject Attitudes toward International Affairs: A Pilot Study." *Experimental Study of Politics,* 4, 1, February:36-54.

Wilson, E. O. (1975) *Sociobiology: The New Synthesis.* Cambridge: Harvard University Press.

Wilson, E. (1938) *My Memoir.* Indianapolis: Bobbs-Merrill.

# 5
# The Biology
# of International Relations

Perhaps no association seems as remote as that between biology and international relations. It is usually assumed that the "high politics" that so often characterizes relations between nations assures the isolation of international affairs from the more mundane aspects of political life. Such an assumption, however, belies the rather substantial amount of work that has been done by students of biopolitics in examining the behavior of actors in the international system.

Some of this early work grew out of the awful physical and emotional toll taken by the events of World War II. So destructive was that war that writers frequently reflected upon the reasons why man could adopt such violent behavior. Work of the time focused on the pathological tensions in individuals that were described as a form of human illness (e.g., Kisker, 1951). It was not uncommon to find scholars suggesting that the human race had entered the early stages of collective insanity.

Such orientations, however, did little to shift the study of international relations in biological directions. Peterson and Somit (n.d.), for example, point out that between 1967 and 1971, only 30 percent of the basic world politics textbooks contained references to biological materials. Though that percentage increased to 43 between 1972 and 1976, such references were, for the most part, sketchy allusions without any sensitivity to the impact that substantive aspects of the life sciences might have on the study of international relations.

Two notable exceptions to this lack of a trend should be mentioned. Mills (1973), reflecting the emerging public policy emphasis, pointed out that much of what we call modern international relations has a decidedly biological flavor. Peacetime issues such as food supply, reproduction, human adaptability, competition, and change are intimately related to the study of international relations, and coincidentally are also exciting subjects in the contemporary life sciences. Indeed, "by his enormous control over his environment man tends to think that he has escaped from most biological limitations; but [as] with most rapid changes in the last half century, evidence has emerged to suggest that basic biological processes may be playing a much greater part in human affairs than we would like to think" (Mills, 1973:316).

The other exception is Pettman (1975), who in his study of human behavior in international relations has surveyed some of the literature of biopolitics, the life sciences, and ethology. However, neither Mills nor Pettman comes to grips with the reasonably extensive basic literature on the biopolitics of international relations.

Though many of the observations discussed in the chapters on the political system and elites are applicable to the study of world politics, in the present chapter we want to focus much more specifically on the aspects of international relations that have been explored with a biological orientation. In doing so we will examine the biological dimensions of the nation, the international system, and a range of other factors related to the study of the international crisis.

## The Nation as a Primary Unit

Students of international relations are well aware that the primary unit of analysis in the field has been, at least in the modern period, the nation-state. Most textbooks have assumed that nations are the building blocks and the actors of the international system. It is also generally assumed that nationalism is the "essence" of the modern nation-state. While we have not universally accepted definition of nationalism,

Kohn's (1967:16) classic definition comes closest to describing those elements that most scholars would agree must be included in any definition: nationalism is "a state of mind permeating the large majority of people and [that] claims to permeate all its members; it recognizes the nation-state as the ideal form of political organization and the nationality as the source of all creative cultural energy and economic well-being." Other factors such as shared history, language, territory, and culture are often included as nonessential aspects of nationalism.

The key element in the concept of nationalism is the state of mind that permeates the majority of the members of the nation. It is just this state of mind that intrigued Willhoite. Though not speaking to the concept of nationalism directly, Willhoite (1977) has argued that humanity's evolutionary past might provide a firm basis for understanding what he calls "collective intolerance" or, on an organized basis, "systems of official intolerance." Collective intolerance is defined as a situation in which "members of a group . . . [expect] and . . . [insist] upon behavioral and intellectual conformity within the collectivity with which they identify. . . . Concomitantly, "they [reject] or [suppress] types of persons, behavior, or symbolic expressions which they perceive as not conforming to group norms" (Willhoite, 1977:667).

How might collective intolerance, which is in such evidence on virtually all levels of human affairs but especially within the nation, have come about? Willhoite (1977) argues that the evolutionary heritage of Homo sapiens appears to provide the best answers to this question. Human beings are superbly adaptable creatures who, like other species, evolved intimate social groups that provided protection against interlopers or predators. Collective intolerance, then, "enhance[d] the solidarity, cohesiveness, and effectiveness of the social group with which the individual primarily indentifie[d]" (Willhoite, 1970:677). Furthermore, since early humans lived in small hunting and gathering groups, they sought and depended upon the "mutual dependability, predictability of responses, and reinforcement of essential bonds [which] would have

assumed overriding urgency in species requiring for survival
the co-ordinated sharing of protective efforts, work and food
among all members of a group" (Willhoite, 1977:679). Thus it
is not unreasonable to suggest that human beings might be
genetically programmed to respect authority that is associated
with enhancing security. In addition, says Willhoite (1977:
680), "each individual's susceptibility to behavioral and symbolic socialization may largely account for the effectiveness of a
central teaching of both religious and secular moral ideologies
in complex societies" such as "the duty of self-sacrifice and
other altruistic acts for the sake of one's non-kin or collective
abstractions." These abstractions might include such notions
as the fatherland, the nation, democracy, or peace.

A nation, then, might be conceptualized as an organized,
authoritative system of intolerance that is a form of association
in human societies suggested by genetic heritage. There
appears to be good evolutionary evidence upon which to build
such a case.

It might be argued, however, that the nation-state is a
relatively modern phenomenon and that we do not appear to
account for previous historical situations in which the church,
noblemen, landlords, emperors, etc. were the central authorities in larger human groupings. There appears to be no
conflict between this observation and an evolutionary perspective. Homo sapiens has apparently evolved into an allegiance-
owing creature. Recorded history provides us with successive
and differing objects of allegiance; but allegiance as a phenomenon appears consistent. The contemporary period is witnessing
a situation in which human allegiance is to the nation.

*Territoriality*

Territoriality is often associated with nationhood. Most
scholars treat the idea of territoriality as a legalistic concept,
which indeed it has become. In the literature of ethology or
animal social behavior the idea of territoriality has been
developed by Lorenz (1966) and Eibl-Eibesfeldt (1970) as an
attribute of biobehavioral life, quite removed from any
legalistic connotation. Citing Tinbergen (1971), Pettman

(1975:192) points out that territoriality may have its evolutionary origin in the "attack and withdrawal behavior which defines animal boundaries, and the group territorialism that man still carries with him as part of his 'animal heritage' from the time when he was a hunting primate organized in social groups." More precise and original work needs to be done by political scientists to explore comprehensively the biopolitical roots of human territoriality. Such research, if done with a biological awareness, should provide a new understanding of the territorial basis of contemporary nationhood. However, when that work is done, it must be serious scientific research and not the selective, impressionistic type that has marked the published offerings of some (e.g., Ardrey, 1966).

### Personal Deviance and International Conflict

Students of international politics have frequently shown concern for the apparent relationship between affairs or conditions within the nation and foreign policy behavior. Haas (1968) has attempted to determine whether strain within a society might be correlated with the society's tendency to choose military instruments as tools of statecraft. Indicators of strain within a society can be looked upon as elements of personal deviance such as homicide, alcoholism, and suicide. "Homicide represents rebelliousness directed at social targets; suicide is a passive orientation to strain directed at a person; alcoholism is a withdrawal with respect to social norms" (Haas, 1968:222). Military aspects of foreign policy include participation in war, military expenditures, and the frequency of entry into international aggression. Haas (1968:219) hypothesized that "if national aggressiveness is related to societal strain, then one would expect rates of deviance to be on the upswing as a decision to go to war is made by a state's decision makers."

In order to test this hypothesis, Haas collected data for ten states during a sixty-year time period. While this brief review does not do justice to the complexity of Haas's findings, some of his general conclusions can be reported here. He found that "suicide increases precede upswings in military expenditures; but if homicide or alcoholism deaths increase, military expenditures decline." Moreover, "if suicide is much more common than other violent deviance in a country, military expenditures climb, war participation is more frequent, but wars are less aggressively entered. . . . As alcoholism displaces homicide as a more frequent form of deviance in a country, military expenditures are increased" (Haas, 1968:243). However, the hypothesis that societal stress precedes the use of military instruments in the international arena was not supported.

The value of Haas's work, aside from his specific findings, is that he has shown that it is indeed possible as well as productive for a political scientist to utilize biologically related variables in aggregate data analysis in order to study the international behavior of states. Further, Haas's efforts indicate that more complete explanations of foreign policies require analysts to broaden their perspectives beyond the "traditional" variables of international political analysis and into the more human-oriented indices of the life sciences. Corning's "survival indicators" mentioned in Chapter 2, if coupled with an orientation such as Haas's might jointly produce the kind of monitoring framework that has been suggested so often as an early warning of difficulty within the international system.

## Biological Models of the International System

While nation-state actors exist, they also interact with each other. These patterns of interaction are normally thought of as creating a system of relationships referred to as an international system. Students of international relations are familiar with the variety of models that purport either to describe previous and existing systems or to conceptualize future systemic possibilities. Traditionally, these models have been based on rather mechanistic conceptualizations utilizing such imagery, for example, as the chandelier to describe a multipolar balance of power system or a seesaw to illustrate a biopolar system. Wenner (1970), however, has suggested that more powerful explanatory models might be developed by examining the interactive patterns of living organisms. He has indicated that far from being merely allegorical or illustrative, an examination of such patterns may reveal real isomorphisms.

Table 5.1 displays, in outline form, eight types of biological interaction patterns. Some of these patterns, though similar to political interactions, do contain significant differences which might be briefly discussed. This discussion leans heavily on Wenner (1970:6-9).

Neutralism, while a familiar concept to a political scientist, conveys something quite different to a biologist: the absence of a relationship. Competition refers to a relationship in which actors contest for limited resources that in the animal world include land, water, food, etc.

Wenner indicates that parasitism and predation are often difficult to differentiate. Both interactions are exploitive: in the case of parasitism it is not in the interest of the parasite to bring about the demise of its host; while in predation the predator is insensitive to the victim's existence. Relationships between developing and developed nations, for example, might be analyzed with models of parasitism and/or predation.

Amensalism is a relationship in which the mere presence of an actor limits the freedom of action of another actor. Finland is an example of a nation whose foreign policy has been dramatically affected by the presence of the Soviet Union adjacent to its borders.

An interactive pattern that is essential for one party but marginal for the other is referred to as commensalism. Superpower relationships with minor states might fall into this category.

Proto-cooperation is a patterned relationship in which mutuality is maintained only as long as the interaction is beneficial to both participants. The key aspect of proto-cooperation is that neither party is irreparably harmed if the relationship terminates. An example of this might be a shift by one nation of its mix of purchases in the international marketplace.

Wenner reserves his keenest interest for the interactive pattern of symbiosis or mutualism. In this pattern both parties in the relationship profit from the interaction, which is necessary and obligatory. It is obligatory in the sense that the association is essential to the survival of the symbionts. Within a sym-

TABLE 5.1

INTERACTION PATTERNS AND THEIR EFFECTS ON POPULATIONS 'A' and 'B'*

| Type of Interaction | Effect When Interacting | | Result of Interaction ** |
|---|---|---|---|
| | A | B | |
| 1. NEUTRALISM (A and B are independent) | 0 | 0 | Neither groups affects the status, etc. of the other |
| 2. COMPETITION (A and B are competitors) | - (+) | - (+) | Group most affected is weakened, depleted, etc. (Positive effects of competition are possible.) |
| 3. PARASITISM (A is parasite, B is host) | + | - | Obligatory for A; B is inhibited, adversely affected (as an individual; B population could achieve some benefit). |
| 4. PREDATION (A is predator, B is prey) | + | - | |
| 5. AMENSALISM (A is amensal, B is the inhibitor, restrictor) | - | 0 | A is inhibited, restricted; B is not affected |
| 6. COMMENSALISM (A is commensal, B is host) | + | 0 | Obligatory/necessary for A; B is not affected |
| 7. PROTO-COOPERATION (A and B are cooperators) | + | + | Interaction favorable to both, but not necessary |
| 8. SYMBIOSIS (MUTUALISM) (A and B are symbionts) | + | + | Interactions benefit both, and necessary or obligatory |

* Effect Scale of Interactions:

0 = No Effect
+ = Positive, Functional, Beneficial Effect
- = Negative, Dysfunctional, Non-Beneficial Effect

** For the sake of clarity, and to provide a set of potential parameters which may be objectively verified, it may be suggested that these interactions could be measured in terms of:

(1) the "survival" of the species and its members (i.e., life/death); and

(2) the "survival" of a species-specific or inter-species structure or "regular" pattern of association.

Source: Adapted from Odum, 1959:226, cited in Wenner, 1970:5.

biotic relationship, evolutionary change can take place that might have differential effects upon the participants or even terminate the relationship altogether. Biologists who study symbiotic relationships emphasize the functions that the symbionts perform for one another. "One of the complicating factors in such analyses is that the interaction of two organisms may, over time, involve an increasing number of activities, with each specialized adjustment entailing a decreased adaptability to new or different conditions" (Wenner, 1970:11).

It might be useful to provide possible examples of symbiotic relationships in the international arena, keeping in mind that political scientists cannot define symbiosis as rigorously as biologists. Efforts directed toward political or economic integration, such as the European Economic Community (EEC), might be looked upon as an attempt to create a symbiotic relationship. Dependencies among the participants are fostered within a context of self-interest. The Arab-Israeli conflict can also be looked upon as a symbiosis even though it is an antagonistic relationship. The symbionts in this relationship have justified and shaped their domestic and international policies in terms of the symbiosis. Wenner (1970:18) points out that "if one were to use the prevailing terminology of political science one would employ a different conceptual framework for the analysis and description of each of these two cases. On the other hand, [he] venture[s] to suggest that there are characteristics common to these two issues, and that current taxonomies and analytical frameworks ignore these similarities." Thus, in the case of both the EEC and the Arab-Israeli conflict all the symbionts achieve benefits from the relationship. It is only by using a symbiotic model to examine the relationship that a comprehensive and complete understanding of the issues involved can be derived.

This brief description of eight biological patterns of association does not begin to reveal the intricacies of each of the interactive models. Such work, however, appears so promising that it would be unfortunate if scholars were not to apply these models to additional problems, issues, and relationships within the international system.

**The International Crisis**

The behavior of nations and statesmen during international crises has long been of interest to students of international relations. (This section borrows from my previous work on crisis. See Wiegele, 1973; Wiegele and Plowman, 1974; and Wiegele, 1976, 1977, 1978, and 1979.) Crises are serious international events that frequently mark historic turning points in the relationships between nations. It should come as no surprise, then, that a considerable literature regarding crisis has developed during the post–World War II period. Much of this work has been collected in Hermann (1972) and assessed in Young (1977).

It is during crisis situations where the normal processes of government are frequently not utilized that the influence of individual-level variables come into a special prominence (Holsti, 1976:29-31). During these kinds of decisional situations the effects of stress become pronounced in elites (Holsti and George, 1976). While politically oriented research has dealt with stress in crisis, most of that work has focused on psychological effects. Two studies that have attempted to broaden the consideration of stress into the arenas of illness (Torre, 1964) and interpersonal conflicts (Druckman, 1973) have indirectly but inadequately dealt with biological factors.

*A Model of Stress*

In attempting to reconcile differences between biological and psychological models of stress, I have suggested a model that might be able to guide future research efforts in a more realistic manner. Leaning heavily on Holsti and George (1976) I defined stress as the anxiety, fear, and/or biophysiological change that develops as the internal response of an individual to an external load placed upon it by a pathogenic agent, stressor, or life crisis that is perceived as posing a severe threat to one or more values of a political decision maker. Utilizing such a definition, a model was developed that allows an analyst to take into account both biological and psychological variables.

While some of the elements of the above definition of stress will be discussed later in this chapter, a word regarding "life crises" might be in order. Holmes and Rahe (1967:216) have developed what they refer to as a "social readjustment rating scale" that ranks normal life events by stress values. For example, of over forty events, the ten beginning with the highest stress are: death of a spouse, divorce, marital separation, jail term, death of a close family member, personal injury or illness, marriage, dismissal from one's job, marital reconciliation, and retirement from work. In the most rudimentary terms, researchers have attempted to show relationships between the occurrence of cumulative stressful life events and the onset of physical and mental illness. In general a variety of correlates have been identified; among them are coronary heart disease, acute schizophrenia, depression, suicide attempts, neuroses, and general health.

Using the knowledge of stressful *life* events and the definition of stress above, it is possible to advance a model of stress based upon the period of time a leader spends in office. That period can be viewed as one of stress susceptibility in which stressful *political* events impact on an individual decision maker. If a scale of stressful political events were developed comparable to the stressful life events scale, it might be possible to predict the onset of illness in a way that would minimize its impact on decisional behavior.

In an even more complex endeavor, it might be possible to utilize both a stressful life events scale and a stressful political events scale in an attempt to fully understand the totality of pressures confronting a decision maker during an international crisis situation. Such an orientation would relate a leader's personal life to his political life in an empirically rigorous way.

The following discussion will emphasize biological and medical influences and try to point out relationships to various psychological aspects of crisis. Bear in mind that we are examining stress because it is so intimately related to the behavior of foreign policy elites during international crisis.

## Stress and Health

Contemporary human beings are the product of a long evolutionary history. During that history they have frequently confronted threats to their existence. In his now classic work, Cannon (1929) identified the physiological changes that take place in a human organism during periods of substantial stress. Such changes bring forth adrenalin and sugar into the bloodstream; the heart beats faster, the lungs operate more efficiently, and the muscles are infused with blood. These are the anticipatory responses to stress that prepare an organism for "fight or flight." Early Homo sapiens, confronted by a multitude of threats to personal safety from the natural environment, was readied for action by a set of physiological anticipatory preparations. Threatened individuals either fled their challengers or they remained to fight. In either choice, however, the physiological preparations noted by Cannon resulted in an outcome requiring muscular exertion. Such exertion produced a cathartic result for the threatened person.

In the contemporary era, we are not confronted by continuous threats to our personal physical existence. Nevertheless, the anticipatory mobilization of physiological processes does take place during periods of stress such as those confronted by foreign policy decision makers during international crisis situations. Thus, an individual is aroused for fight or flight response for which no appropriate physical action can take place in modern, human social settings. As Hamburg (1961:278) has pointed out, "the very rapid cultural changes of modern times have made our environment so radically different from those in which we evolved that some of our biological equipment is obsolete and perhaps even maladaptive."

With their heavy role responsibilities, heads of state and other centrally located foreign policy elites are subjected to intense stresses during international crises. Such stresses, which cannot be physiologically discharged as nature evidentally intended, produce the wearing effects of office that are so visible on the faces of elites over the course of their administrations.

Stress can also be manifested in the work style of Western elites. Minc (1966) has indicated that individuals who display a "high degree of occupational leadership" in Western societies exhibit a broad time perspective, are self-disciplined and self-directed, are detached from immediate gratification, sublimate emotional influences, and are reliable and self-driven in achieving goals to which deadlines are attached. While these factors certainly characterize successful elite behavior they also, unfortunately, correlate positively with a profile of the coronary-prone individual. Thus the demands of the Western-oriented work style can lead individual political actors into postures that are clearly threatening to their health. The physiological arousal and the situational demands during the international crisis are so strong that participants in decision making have on occasion suffered serious psychological breakdowns (Kennedy, 1969:22).

## General Physical Fitness

Human beings may have evolved in such a way as to require rigorous physical exertion of the muscular structure in order to maintain a healthy level of fitness. And while the physically fit are much admired in contemporary society, this "ideal" is undermined by labor saving devices resulting from our high technology civilization. These devices have created a situation in which a sedentary life style may well be the "norm" of physical existence. The diffusion of technology in the twentieth century has taken place so quickly that evolutionary processes appear not to have addressed the relationship between Homo sapiens as a physical being and Homo sapiens in a sedentary culture. As we stated above, it is during the abbreviated periods of international crisis resolution that the characteristics of individuals come into bold relief and play a substantially greater role in decisional behavior than they might in routine bureaucratic decisions. This observation appears to hold for general physical fitness.

With regard to international crisis Milburn (1972:264) has written that, "Chief among the effects of stress that have been reported from both laboratory and field studies are tiredness and sheer physical fatigue resulting from depletion of the adrenals. If continued long enough, fatigue leads to increased irritability, to subclinical paranoid reactions, to heightened suspiciousness, hostility, and increased defensiveness." In examining the literature relating stress tolerance to fitness levels, Wiegele and Plowman (1974:77) found "evidence supporting the fact that psychological and emotional situations are stressors for the human organism and can thereby cause a multiplicity of physiological changes and adjustments." Indeed, a state of strong anxiety can cause deleterious distortions in the human cardiovascular system. A strengthening of the cardiovascular system, therefore, is exceedingly important for political decision makers in high stress situations that are normally accompanied by high anxiety states. The key observation here is that increased resistance to the effects of psychological stress during crisis periods can be accomplished in substantial measure by rigorous physical training. Thus, President Kennedy's swimming interludes in the White House pool during the Cuban missile crisis may have been highly functional for efficient and restrained decision making.

It should be emphasized that the Kennedy example might be misleading in that it seems to point to an isolated act of physical activity during a difficult decisional situation. Evidence in the human life sciences suggests that high levels of fitness can be obtained only by regular physical exertion. Thus, leaders who are called upon to contribute enormous amounts of physical and emotional energy during short time periods should be encouraged to make every attempt at maintaining good levels of physical fitness. If they are fit, they will be able to withstand the stresses of crisis much more efficiently and positively.

## Age

Age is another factor that can have an impact on decisional behavior during an international crisis. Foreign policy decision makers are generally older and more experienced than others. Paige (1968:367), for example, found that the average age of the fifteen men who participated in the decision to intervene in Korea was fifty-three years. The reasons for this are not difficult to deduce. Promotional processes within the Department of State are notoriously slow, thereby virtually guaranteeing that only "thoroughly matured" officials will occupy the higher ranks of the foreign affairs bureaucracy. But, perhaps more importantly, since presidential candidates are normally in their late fifties when nominated for that office, they probably tend to pick age-compatible advisors. Whatever the reason, in foreign affiars age appears to be an analytical consideration.

The White House Conference on Aging (1971:18) has observed that "the most characteristic physiological manifestation of aging is the progressive diminution of the ability of the individual to withstand stress." This becomes evident in changes in sense acuity, alertness, psychomotor skills, comprehension of data, risk taking, and choice behavior. But age considerations must be balanced. On the positive side are the decision maker's experience, maturity, caution, sense of responsibility, and emotional stability. Negatively, there are the tendencies toward overconfidence and extreme choices, difficulty with complex systems or situations, weakness in short-term memory, and difficulty in decoding problems. Current biologically oriented research on the behavioral effects of the aging process should ultimately allow political analysts to test propositions regarding the influence of age on decisional behavior, especially as it relates to crisis.

## Circadian and Diurnal Rhythms

Certain rhythms or "biological days" in the human species are regulated by internal biological mechanisms. Such time periods, which often approximate twenty-four hours, are referred to as circadian rhythms from the Latin *circa dies*, meaning about a day in length. Diurnal rhythms are those based on a day-night cycle.

Circadian rhythms are in evidence in pulse rate, blood pressure, body temperature, and many other biological processes. Some adrenal hormones, for example corticosteroids (the stress hormones), are secreted in a rhythmic fashion, with larger amounts released into the bloodstream between 6 and 8 a.m. and the lowest amounts after midnight. The physiological effects of the corticosteroids are not felt until several hours later when they produce subtle behavioral changes. This implies that decision makers might be able to withstand the effects of stress earlier in their working day rather than later.

Physiological periodicity is also much in evidence when travellers cross time zones in jet aircraft. The resulting circadian disorganization can often be profound, producing feelings of anxiousness and fatigue. These effects could influence that course of international negotiations, especially those that take place during periods when diplomats are shuttling between capitals during abbreviated negotiating sessions, leaving little time for the readjustment of rhythms.

Circadian disorganization might also be in evidence during an international crisis in which two or more nations in widely divergent time zones are locked in a critical confrontation. It is possible that one or both nations' decision makers might fall victim to the effects of circadian disorganization, which of course includes fatigue. It is unrealistic, of course, to caution leaders not to allow themselves to become subjected to the stresses of alterations in periodicity. Crises develop at times that are accidental to the biological rhythms of leaders. However, one should not discount the possibility that a biologically aware group of decision makers could attempt to manipulate the physiological states of an opposing group during a short-lived crisis by forcing them to deal with issues on a schedule that would be destabilizing to their circadian rhythms. Such efforts might be able to exacerbate the state of fatigue that normally accompanies crisis decision making, thereby producing an advantage to the manipulating nation.

### Remote Psychophysiological Monitoring during International Crisis

Many analysts have attempted to show relationships between the psychological, state of a leader and his subsequent decisional behavior. In attempting to link these two factors, however, researchers are usually confronted by the immediate problem of acquiring scientifically reliable data. Normally, leaders will not submit themselves to the intrusion of a paper-and-pencil psychological test, nor, for obvious political reasons, will they participate in psychoanalytic interviews. If this is true on the level of domestic politics, it is even more the case in international relations: foreign policy elites tend to be inaccessible, especially during international crises. Consequently, an analytic technique that can be employed remotely and unobtrusively would be particularly useful in assessing the psychological states of elites.

The psychological stress evaluator (PSE) is an electronic instrument that identifies, measures, and displays in graphic form certain stress-related components of the human voice without the direct use of any sensors. This instrument has been utilized in a variety of experimental and applied research settings (Borgen and Goodman, 1976; Brenner, Branscomb, and Schwartz, 1978; and Wiggins, McCranie, and Bailey, 1975). Because the PSE analyzes the human voice, a simple audio recording of a speaker is the only raw data necessary to utilize the instrument.

When an individual experiences psychological stress, unconscious changes in the electronic configuration of the voice occur. These manifestations of stress result from a slight tensing of the vocal cords that occurs even under conditions of minor stress. A dampening of selected frequency variations then takes place. All of this is electronically decipherable because a normal tape recording preserves the speech pattern containing the configurations of stress. Using electronic filtering and frequency discrimination techniques, the PSE processes the voice frequencies and displays the inaudible stess-related patterns or traces on a moving, heat sensitive strip chart. Figure 5.1 represents a display of three unstressed words. Figure 5.2 illustrates traces of three highly stressed words.

A researcher employing the PSE prepares a trace for each word in a narrative document. In international crisis research, words on which a speaker exhibits high stress indicate discomfort or negativeness regarding the concept. Up to this point, analysis has remained on the paragraph or theme level, and so words are aggregated by theme rather than analyzed individually. In effect, this is a method of physiologically based content analysis at the paragraph level.

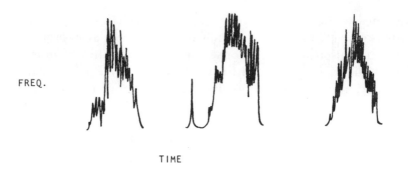

FREQ.

TIME

FIGURE 5.1    Three unstressed word recordings

Voice analysis is an appropriate technique to study the behavior of leaders in international crisis, particularly since heads of state normally request support from and report to their national populations during these serious international situations. Leaders can be looked upon as leaking signals beyond the manifest meanings of language (Wiegele, 1979). These signals can be captured and appraised using methods and techniques that are based essentially on certain biological realities.

Five speeches of U.S. presidents during crisis situations were analyzed with the PSE (Wiegele, 1978): Truman on Korea (1950), Kennedy on Berlin (1961) and on Cuba (1962), and Johnson on the Gulf of Tonkin (1964) and the *Pueblo* (1968). All of the speeches in this study contained one or more paragraphs that underlined the theme that the United States was determined to resolve the crisis successfully, i.e., in its own interests. When the determination theme exceeded the mean stress level for the crisis document as a whole, we inferred that the speaker viewed the situation as critical, dangerous, and possibly leading to war. This was true for Korea, Berlin, and Cuba. Conversely, when determination themes were low in stress, as was the case on Tonkin and the *Pueblo*, it is likely that the speaker perceives that situation as minimally threatening to his nation, and therefore less willing to run risks that could lead to war.

Crisis speeches also contain what might be categorized as precipitating act themes. We viewed the precipitating act as a

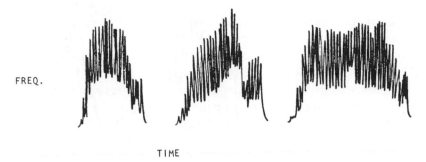

FIGURE 5.2    Three highly stressed word recordings

stimulus configuration or event in the external environment of a nation that became the occasion for a national response by a central decision maker and produced in him a level of physiological arousal that could be ascertained by voice analysis. PSE data of the precipitating act statements revealed them to be low stress themes. In only one of our five crises, the Gulf of Tonkin, did the precipitating act theme come through as a high stress theme. It is not unreasonable to assume that leaders view precipitating acts as "givens" or facts beyond dispute. They cause little psychological stress in a speaker because they are accepted as unambiguous challenges. In the case of the Gulf of Tonkin, the fact of an aggressive attack by the North Vietnamese on the *USS Maddox* was apparently not established beyond doubt, hence the uncertainty in President Johnson's voice was displayed as high stress.

In the work on the five crises, voice stress analysis did appear to be tapping the underlying emotional states of the presidents who were examined. The psychophysiological data did fall into patterns that were meaningful in terms of the crises examined. Thus, the PSE does appear to hold the possibility of becoming a powerful tool of remote assessment.

## Conclusions

Clearly, there are numerous aspects of the study of international relations that could profit from the inclusion of a biological orientation. These range from questions of basic research to major issue areas of international public policy. Given the continuing interest of scholars in modelling the international system, the utilization of biological models for this purpose might be highly productive. Crisis management processes will undoubtedly profit from an awareness of several biological clusters of information regarding the impact of stress on the human organism. In the realm of public policy, the new issues that confront and will continue to confront international organizations as well as nation-states will require an increasingly large reservoir of biological knowledge if resolution is to be forthcoming.

## References

Ardrey, R. (1966) *The Territorial Imperative*. New York: Atheneum.

Borgen, L. A. and L. I. Goodman. (1976) *Audio Stress Analysis*. Ann Arbor: Park Davis Research Laboratories.

Brenner, M., H. Branscomb, and G. E. Schwartz. (1978) "Psychological Stress Evaluator: Two Tests of a Vocal Measure." *Psychophysiology*.

Cannon, W. B. (1929) *Bodily Changes in Pain, Hunger, Fear, and Rage*. New York: Appleton-Century-Crofts.

Druckman, D. (1973) *Human Factors in International Negotiations: Social Psychological Aspects of International Conflict*. Sage Professional Paper in International Studies. Beverly Hills: Sage.

Eibl-Eibesfeldt, I. (1970) *Ethology*. New York: Holt, Rinehart, and Winston.

Haas, M. (1968) "Social Change and National Aggressiveness, 1900-1960," in J. D. Singer, ed., *Quantitative International Politics*. New York: Free Press.

Hamburg, D. (1961) "The Relevance of Recent Evolutionary Changes to Human Stress Biology," in S. L. Washburn, ed., *Social Life of Early Man*. Chicago: Aldine.

Hermann, C. F. (1972) *International Crisis: Insights from Behaviorial Research*. New York: Free Press.

Holmes, T. H. and R. H. Rahe. (1967) "The Social Readjustment Rating Scale." *Journal of Psychosomatic Research* 11: 213-218.

Holsti, O. (1976) "Foreign Policy Formulation Viewed Cognitively," in R. Axelrod, ed., *Structure of Decision: The Cognitive Maps of Political Elites.* Princeton: Princeton University Press.

Holsti, O. and A. L. George. (1976) "The Effects of Stress on the Performance of Foreign Policy Makers," in C. P. Cotter, ed., *Political Science Annual* 6. Indianapolis: Bobbs-Merrill.

Kennedy, R. F. (1969) *Thirteen Days.* New York: Norton.

Kisker, G. W., ed. (1951) *World Tension: The Psychology of International Relations.* New York: Prentice-Hall.

Kohn, H. (1967) *The Idea of Nationalism: A Study in Its Origins and Background.* New York: Macmillan.

Lorenz, K. (1966) *On Aggression.* London: Methuen.

Milburn, T. (1972) "The Management of Crises," in C. Hermann, ed., *International Crises: Insights from Behavioral Research.* New York: Free Press.

Mills, I. H. (1973) "Biological Factors in International Relations." *Yearbook of World Affairs* 17:316-331.

Minc, S. (1966) "Civilized Pattern of Activity, Cardiac Adaptation, and Ischemic Heart Disease," in W. Raab, ed., *Prevention of Ischemic Heart Disease.* Springfield, Ill.: Charles A. Thomas.

Odum, E. (1959) *Fundamentals of Ecology*, 2nd edition. Philadelphia: W. B. Saunders.

Paige, G. (1968) *The Korean Decision.* New York: Free Press.

Peterson, S. A. and A. Somit. (n.d.) "International Politics: Toward A Biological Perspective." Unpublished manuscript.

Pettman, R. (1975) *Human Behavior and World Politics.* New York: St. Martin's Press.

Tinbergen, N. (1971) "On War and Peace—Animals and Man," in H. Fredrich, ed., *Man and Animal.* London: Paladin.

Torre, M. (1964) "How Does Physical and Mental Illness Influence Negotiations Between Diplomats?" *International Journal of Social Psychiatry*, Summer.

Wenner, M. (1970) "Symbiosis and Politics: Notes Toward the Use of of Biological Models in Political Science." Paper presented Eighth Congress of the International Political Science Association, Munich, West Germany, August.

White House Conference on Aging. (1971) *Physical and Mental Health: Background Issues.* Washington, D.C.: U.S. Government Printing Office.

Wiegele, T. C. (1979) "Signal Leakage and the Remote Psychological Assessment of Foreign Policy Elites," in L. Falkowski, ed., *Psychological Models in International Politics.* Boulder, Co.: Westview Press.

———. (1978) "The Psychophysiology of Elite Stress in Five International Crises: A Preliminary Test of a Voice Measurement Technique." *International Studies Quarterly,* December.

———. (1977a) "Models of Stress and Disturbances in Elite Political Behaviors: Psychological Variables and Political Decision Making," in R. S. Robins, ed., *Psychopathology and Political Leadership.* New Orleans: Tulane Studies in Political Science 16, pp. 79-111.

———. (1977b) "Physiologically-Based Content Analysis: An Application in Political Communication," in B. Ruben, ed., *Communication Yearbook II.* New Brunswick, N.J.: Transaction Books.

———. (1976) "Health and Stress during International Crisis: Neglected Input Variables in the Foreign Policy Decision-Making Process." *Journal of Political Science,* Spring: 139-144.

———. (1973) "Decision Making in an International Crisis: Some Biological Factors." *International Studies Quarterly* 17, 3, September.

Wiegele, T. C. and S. Plowman. (1974) "Stress Tolerance and International Crisis: The Significance of Biologically-Oriented Experimental Research to the Behavior of Political Decision Makers." *Experimental Study of Politics* 3, 3, December:63-92.

Willhoite, F. H. Jr. (1977) "Evolution and Collective Intolerance." *Journal of Politics* 39:667-685.

Wiggins, S. L., M. McCranie, and P. Bailey. (1975) "Assessment of Voice Stress in Children." *Journal of Nervous and Mental Disease* 160.

Young, R. (1977) "International Crisis: Progress and Prospects for Applied Forecasting and Management." A special issue of the *International Studies Quarterly* 21, 1, March.

# 6

# The Biopolitics of Human Conflict

Students of political behavior have had a continuing interest in human conflict, aggression, and war. Several excellent works have reviewed this literature recently (e.g., Dougherty and Pfaltzgraff 1971, and Pettman, 1975) and a variety of anthologies exploring various dimensions have appeared (e.g., Nettleship, Givens, Nettleship, 1975). Other works such as Coser (1956) and McNeil (1965) have become classic texts.

Our concern is to inquire whether a biopolitical approach can assist political scientists in developing a more accurate and a more human understanding of the phenomenon of political conflict. The biopolitical approach provides an interdisciplinary perspective; in this regard it is not unusual in conflict studies. Virtually all disciplines that have an interest in human behavior have pursued the study of conflict with a good deal of persistence. In addition to biology and political science, these disciplines include psychology, economics, business, history, anthropology, sociology, and communications. Most political scientists who have studied conflict have felt reasonably comfortable in incorporating perspectives from the other social sciences as well as psychology, especially social psychology, in their work.

On the other hand, to adopt an interdisciplinary perspective that includes in an operational way the substantive findings of the life sciences has been particularly difficult for the political researcher. As a result, relatively little biopolitical work on the topic of conflict has been produced, but what has been done has

introduced the discipline to such an orientation, has sketched
out a possible research paradigm for studying human
aggression in evolutionary terms, and has produced several
powerful empirical efforts with a more restricted focus. It is to
this work that we now turn.

## The Nature of Conflict, Violence, and Aggression

"Conflict," wrote Dougherty and Pfaltzgraff (1971:139) in
reference to politics, "is an interaction involving humans, . . .
conflict implies more than mere competition." These writers
assert that "conflict usually refers to a condition in which one
identifiable group of human beings (whether tribal, ethnic,
linguistic, cultural, religious, socio-economic, political or
other) is engaged in conscious opposition to one or more
identifiable human groups because these groups are pursuing
what are or appear to be incompatible goals." While we all
recognize that human beings engage in conflict, both violent
and nonviolent, we might inquire whether Homo sapiens are
genetically programmed to engage in violence.

The question of whether a particular nation or culture is
prone to conflict or violence has long been of interest to
political analysts and a substantial amount of data has been
collected, aggregated, and analyzed. But this work does not go
to the core of the problem: are human beings naturally
aggressive, conflictful, and violent even though they can
engage in quite the opposite kinds of behavior? One way to
answer this question—which so far has eluded political
scholars—is to "find whether or not there is anything in the
human organism, including therein the central nervous
system, which could be called not a statistical tendency but an
innate, organic predisposition toward violent behavior"
(Davies, 1970:615). Reasoning that culture and history color
our views of human behavior, Davies (1970:615) has suggested
that political scientists explore contemporary scholarship on
the human organism because "it is only in the organism that
each man is like every other man." While critics might view
this as biological reductionism, Davies is cautious to point out

that for him the organism includes psychic, psychological, and emotional qualities and needs as well as the biological. These basic needs, adapted from Maslow, can be modified slightly to include security, knowledge, and a sense of control over one's own destiny.

Davies (1970:615) argues "that the basic needs that all human beings have in common are fundamental instigators to an action sequence which, when severely frustrated, [are] likely to produce aggression, including political violence when government is blamed for the frustration." The basic source of these needs may lie in the human genetic makeup. Research on human needs has focused largely on psychological explanations, with relatively little attention directed toward uncovering neurophysiological origins.

Determining the neurophysiological basis for human needs might appear to be virtually impossible, but Davies points out that physiologists have explored the physical basis of the drives for food and sex. Much of this work has been done with electrical stimulation of the brain (ESB) using animals as subjects. For example, food-satiated animals will begin eating again when food centers of the brain receive electrical stimulation. Early experiments by Cannon and later work by Delgado have located centers in the brain that encourage hostile outlooks and flight or fight reactions.

Neurophysiological factors do not constitute the only possible physical bases of aggressive behavior; the endocrine system too appears to play a role in the process. Two hormones, epinephrine and norepinephrine, are released into the bloodstream during moments of stress. Epinephrine is associated with feelings of anxiety, and norepinephrine with fear.

Because of the relationships between our neurophysiological and endocrine systems, Davies (1970:621)) argues that

it is more reasonable to suppose that most people who have never experienced war and revolution would, in the same circumstances, probably act in the same ways that people in past wars and revolutions have in fact acted. Some people would linger in the background, frightened and withdrawn. Some people would mingle with the crowd or lose themselves in the combat group and fight bravely and savagely, till victory, death, or critical injury. And some people would seek out danger and invite self-sacrifice. Probably most of these people are variously behaving within the broad limits of mental normality.

What is being suggested here is that reactions to certain kinds of social stimuli might be accounted for in large measure by key biological factors. The neurophysiological and endocrine systems, though linked to violent behavior, do not constitute the only causes of such behavior. The manner in which an organism cognitively processes stimuli from the environment clearly plays a role in how the organism will react to a stimulus (Levine and Scotch, 1970:282). Thus, Davies is correct in pointing out that it is important for students of violent political behavior to be aware of both the biological and the psychological ingredients of such activity. As we have stated so often in previous chapters, the expanding body of knowledge about human behavior makes it imperative to incorporate a biological perspective in our studies, especially those of aggression and violence.

### An Evolutionary Theory of Violent Aggression

In discussing the impact of biological factors on mass political behavior (Chapter 3), Davies suggested that there might be a neurological basis for collective memories. In the section above, Davies argued that future research might reveal the locus in the brain of those centers that allow for violent aggression. In a sense, Davies's early work is a prelude to that of Peter Corning (1972, 1973, 1975), who argued that a theory of violent aggression must combine evolutionary considerations, genetic factors, survival consequences, social learning, and observational and experimental evidence. Each of these kinds of data is likely to be generated by researchers working in different disciplines, and we have seemingly returned to the problem of the compartmentalization of scholarship, in this case regarding the study of human aggression. While this observation is probably correct, Corning has advanced a general theory into which the various approaches to the study of violent aggression fit nicely. In utilizing such a theory it will be possible to design imaginative correlational studies that might begin to more precisely focus our investigations of aggression.

Corning (1975:361) accepts Moyer's (1971) eight categories of aggression: predatory, inter-male, fear-induced, irritable, territorial, maternal, instrumental, and sex-related. Because previous work has shown that most aggression is stimulus bound, Moyer's categories are differentiated on the basis of the stimulus configurations in the environment that allow for the release of the aggressive behaviors. Matched with the environmental releasers (or "cue complexes") are apparently specific neural and hormonal substrates within the organism that presumably are a product of evolutionary processes. In the barest terms, stimuli from the environment interacting with the genetically determined characteristics of the organism can produce violent behavior. Thus, "the complex interaction between environmental stimuli, sensory structures, information processing, emotional affect, motor response and even inhibitory or control mechanisms must reflect an interaction among specific internal subsystems and their linkages" (Corning, 1975:361). With this model, each form of violent behavior can be explored holistically, but the task will be much more complex because numerous factors from genetic endowment to observed behavior must be incorporated into the analysis.

It is in his examination of the functions of aggression that Corning's evolutionary perspective is brought to bear most strongly. Reasoning that a phenomenon so widely present in nature as aggression must have been the result of selective processes, Corning argues that at least theoretically, aggression should have some measurable fitness value. As an example, he describes some of his own laboratory experiments on maternal aggression (1975:362):

Female aggression in laboratory strains of the house mouse (*Mus musculus*) is directed primarily against strange male mice, not against cage mates. It is also confined to the period when females are nursing pups. (At other times, the females must be receptive to strange males, for obvious reasons.) So in the course of its evolutionary history, *Mus musculus* (or its ancestor species) evolved internal mechanisms that serve to limit female attacking behaviors for the most part to the period when the females are caring for the young. The function of this form of aggression should be self-evident, but the fitness value has been demonstrated. If not checked, male mice will frequently attack and kill strange mouse pups.

An added value of an evolutionary approach to the study of aggression is that it will allow social scientists to view the phenomenon in a comparative perspective. The aggressive behaviors of all species, including Homo sapiens, can be compared and contrasted in such a way as to ultimately provide a more profound understanding of the meaning and significance of aggression in human political behavior. Thus, when the ubiquitousness of aggression in nature is fully appreciated, it seems likely that theories that focus on aggression as instinctive will become implausible (Corning 1975:363).

It should be pointed out, however, that neither Moyer's categories nor Corning's inclusion of them in an evolutionary paradigm of human aggression satisfactorily explain the existence of collective or group aggression. While collective aggression does exist in the animal world, as political scientists we are centrally concerned with the almost universal distribution of the phenomenon in and between human societies. From an evolutionary perspective, collective aggression is as complex as it is controversial. While this is not the place to spell out the details of this controversy, suffice it to say that analysts are aware of the weak linkages between scholarship on individual aggression and that on group aggression. With this major caveat in mind, let us turn to a brief discussion of possible evolutionary origins and the purposes of human collective aggression.

In Corning's view (1975:364-380), there appear to be numerous causes of collective aggression which range from biologically grounded behavioral propensities to environmental variables and external stimulus configurations. It is possible that collective violence might be traced back to human behaviors such as group bonding practices, territoriality, leader-follower relationships, culture, fear, socioeconomic and ecological circumstances, or problem-solving challenges. Thus, in the human evolutionary past, warfare may have been functionally productive for gaining resources, eliminating threats, regulating population, correcting imbalances in sex ratios, and releasing tensions. Even aggression within a society can be viewed as positively adaptive behavior (Wallace, 1956). "On the evidence to date, then, it seems reasonable to conclude that warfare may have constituted one selecting agent among others in human evolution. This is not the same as saying that wars are desirable, or beneficial. It is merely an assertion that warfare may have played a role in our evolutionary history, for better or worse" (Corning, 1975:373).

Though many of Corning's ideas are conjectural, at least one political scientist has taken serious issue with him. Phillips (n.d.:10) grants that human competitiveness could have been biologically determined. But, he states, implying a distinction between inter- and intra-specific aggression, "it does not follow, however, that that competitiveness *must* have fellow humans as targets, as in warfare." As a matter of fact, before human beings adopted agriculture the anthropological evidence seems to indicate that they directed their aggression toward the hunt. It was only after the availability of wild species declined substantially that early humans displayed aggression toward their fellows. Nevertheless, says Phillips (n.d.:10), "if competitiveness which leads to aggression in killing one's kind is genetically determined in man, then all men ought to engage in it. But we know that, in fact, most individual men do not attempt to kill other men." On the basis of this reasoning which perhaps does not take full account of the variability of human behavior, Phillips concludes that either individuals who kill are biological mutants, or that those who do not kill in spite of their biological endowment for aggression are held in check by cultural prohibitions. In both cases the human propensity for competitiveness appears to be modified by cultural mechanisms.

Another critic of biologically oriented theories of aggression is Timothy Colton (1969), reserving his attack essentially for Lorenz who, he feels, has based his reasoning on animal studies and has failed to take into account the immense power of political ideology in human communities. Further, Colton inquires as to whether aggression is truly a primary behavioral act. Some people, for example, commit aggression for the sake of food; in this instance, aggressiveness is a means to achieve a much more fundamental end. If one examines aggression in terms of basic needs, it is possible that the biological dimensions of aggression might appear in a substantially different light.

## The Individual and Aggression

While it is appropriate to examine the nature and function of collective aggresssion, it is also true that the individual is important in any discussion of human conflict. In Chapter 4 we explored the impact of biological variables on elite behaviors, and in the present chapter we must return, however briefly, to the individual level of analysis. Decisions to go to war or engage in authoritative social conflict are normally the acts of individuals such as heads of state. It is quite true that national populations can be mobilized at a "grass roots" level to exert pressure on decisional structures; nevertheless, decisions are made by individual members of the foreign policy elite and a decision to commit a society war is, at the very least, strongly influenced by the head of state.

Stegenga (1972) has argued that political writers have viewed war in purely rational and "intellectualist" terms, ignoring the unconscious and the nonrational dimensions of decisional behavior. He strongly challenges the "intellectualist bias" and declares bluntly that "decision-making theorists are wrong in neglecting non-rational variables" (Stegenga, 1972:24).

While Stegenga's major interest is in the impact of psychological factors on human aggressiveness, he does feel that certain biologically related factors might be found to influence aggression in important ways. For example, he views war as a means of survival and relates survival needs to the human willingness to struggle over subsistence resources.

Moreover, war can be looked upon as appealing in a nonrational sense because it appears to contribute to the human proclivity for excitement and adventure. Consider this passage from the memoirs of General Matthew B. Ridgway (1956: 218) (but keep in mind that all of us could reflect on our vocations in emotional terms if we chose):

> There was a great deal of sporadic shooting going on, here and there, as the assembling troops hunted the Reds down like rabbits. And I remember feeling that lifting of the spirits, that quickening of the breath and the sudden sharpening of all senses that comes to a man in the midst of battle. It was good to be in action again, good to be lying on the ground with a parachute assault element in the fight. Lynch, I know, enjoyed it as much as I did, the crack of the M-1's, the crump of the incoming mortars—so long, of course, as they didn't get too close (quoted in Stegenga, 1972:33).

Not only do individuals in war develop a deep camaraderie and commitment to undertaking a successful cooperative enterprise, they also are released from personal uncertainties regarding the identification of one's friends and enemies. In exploring Freud's assertion that man is driven by a "death instinct" (Thanatos) to eliminate internal human anxieties, Stegenga (1972:34) suggests, unfortunately with little supporting evidence, that "war offers the opportunity for suicide, either to satisfy an unconscious death wish if one exists, or to escape from the guilt or the problems of a complicated life. War offers suicide without any onus and often with the further comfort that the suicide may be interpreted as heroic."

As we said in the opening of this chapter, there is substantial literature in many disciplines regarding a variety of aspects of aggression, including Freud's theorizing. However, Stegenga's work is of interest because it can be linked so easily to that of political scientists such as Corning, Willhoite, and Schubert who emphasize that in order to understand contemporary political life, we must push deeply into the study of evolutionary biology and human anthropology. What must have been an aura of excitement in the hunting behavior of early Homo sapiens, for example, bears strong resemblance to contemporary descriptions of men in battles and the stimulation that is apparently derived from such experiences.

## Some Specific Applications of Biological Approaches to the Study of Political Conflict and Aggression

The above comments suggest that biological considerations should play an important part in developing a general theory of human conflict and aggression. Let us turn now to some specific and empirically based applications of biological perspective to the study of aggression. We will look at the individual level first and then explore an example of collective activity.

### Physiological Aspects of Aggressive Social Attitudes

Related closely to the work of Wahlke and Lodge on the relationship between attitudes and behavior, which was discussed in Chapter 3, is that of Watts and Sumi. Both of these writers (1976, 1979) and Watts (1976, 1977) have attempted to assess the association between political attitudes as measured by several psychometric scales and various internal physiological changes in subjects during carefully constructed stimulus situations. Two separate experimental studies were undertaken to assess orientations toward aggressive and/or violent behavior.

Watts and Sumi (1979) have expressed concern regarding the problem of directionality in physiological measures. For example, a subject may receive a stimulus, and a physiological response might be recorded, let us say, by measuring galvanic skin conductance. We can determine the amount of change from a baseline that has taken place, but we cannot tell from that measure whether the change was positively or negatively associated with the stimulus. Thus, at least in the much-used galvanic skin response measure, the researcher can assess intensity but not direction.

Recognizing this difficulty, Watts and Sumi (1979) have sought theoretical support for their physiological measures from the work of Lacey and Lacey (1970, 1974) who advanced the "directional fractionation hypothesis." This hypothesis suggests that beat-to-beat heart rate response is negative or positive. In the words of Watts and Sumi (1979:5), "deceleration of heart beat indicates or accompanies attention to external stimuli, or what Lacey refers to as 'stimulus intake'; conversely, acceleration of heart beat is associated with 'stimulus rejection'—the individual's tendency to reject certain stimuli, either to moderate the impact of noxious or aversive stimuli or to reduce sensory input in order to concentrate on a cognitive task." In a study cited by Watts and Sumi, Hare (1973) has confirmed the directional fractionation hypothesis by presenting noxious visual stimuli (pictures of spiders and homicide victims) to subjects and simultaneously monitoring their physiological responses.

With this brief discussion as background, let us look at the first Watts and Sumi study. Using a modified version of Lovibond's CF (Children's F) scale, the researchers (1979:13) hypothesized that "high CF-scorers would show HR (heart rate) acceleration (stimulus rejection)." A high CF score indicates a preference for visual displays of crime and violence. Subjects for the experiment were ten boys and ten girls between the ages of 11 and 14. Their physiological activity was monitored with a polygraph that in this case recorded heart rate and skin conductance responses.

Subjects for the experiment completed a CF scale and items relating to their television viewing habits. After electrodes to monitor heart rate and skin conductance were attached, videotaped scenes from popular television programs were projected for each subject's viewing. These scenes depicted acts of violence from shows such as "The Autobiography of Miss Jane Pittman," "Get Christie Love," and "Police Story." Continuous physiological monitoring took place during the projection of the violent scenes.

The findings indicated that different types of violent scenes produced varying intensities of physiological arousal in subjects. This was explained by surmising that easily understandable situations that were portrayed with dramatic clarity and in which violent acts were directed toward sympathetic characters produced the highest levels of arousal. A further factor also appeared to produce strong reactions in subjects: the intensity of the violence being portrayed in the dramatization.

Even more important than gross reactions to the stimulus material was the analysis of data based on differentiations in scoring on Children's F scale. Lacey's directional fractionation hypothesis was supported by this experiment: violence-accepting subjects experienced heart rate deceleration while violence-rejecting subjects displayed an acceleration in heart rate response. Summing up the basic finding of this experiment, Watts and Sumi (1979:18) observed that "attitude toward violence is related to the type of emotional reaction experienced while reviewing video-taped models of violence and aggressive behavior."

A second study was more complex and involved older subjects, i.e. college students. The basis of this study was the concern and suspicion that television viewing of violence-oriented programs contributed to the lack of empathy for and sensitivity to the plight of fellow human beings. In order to index empathy, Watts and Sumi employed the Mach IV scale developed by Christie and Geis (1970), who constructed this instrument from statements found in Machiavelli's *The Prince*. This scale was designed to measure the qualities of manipulativeness, detachment from affective concern, and cynicism about human behavior. Thus, Watts and Sumi (1979:22) hypothesized that "high Machs would tend toward *lower autonomic arousal* and would tend toward *stimulus intake* rather than stimulus rejection."

However, while the Mach IV scale might measure detachment, aloofness, manipulativeness, and cynicism, it does not provide an assessment of aggressiveness. Therefore, two additional scales were developed: a violence ideology scale designed to measure reactions to social aggression, and a traditionalism scale which, in general, was developed to assess the extent to which a respondent was unsympathetic to those who might challenge the current social order.

Again, as in the first study, Watts and Sumi attempted to show relationships between attitudes and levels of physiological arousal in subjects. "The general hypothesis was that higher acceptance of violence, greater traditionalism, and greater Machiavellianism would all be negatively associated with arousal. That is, individuals who score high on those scales should respond less when confronted with videotaped examples of interpersonal violence" (Watts and Sumi, 1979:26). Put another way, negative attitudes toward violence (i.e., rejection of violence) should be associated with heart rate acceleration, while heart rate deceleration might be characteristic of violence acceptance. It should be mentioned that in this study gender was conceptualized as an independent variable.

The specific findings that resulted from this second study are intriguing. As hypothesized, negative attitudes toward violence and manipulativeness were associated with stimulus rejection. But gender differences appeared in other findings. For example, males responded in the direction of the hypothesis on all measures, but females produced a reverse relationship on the Mach IV scale; and the violence ideology scale resulted in almost no correlation at all. Thus, the Mach scale, in terms of physiological responses, produced opposite associations for males and females. An important general conclusion of this study was that self-assessment of attitudes in paper-and-pencil exercises was not necessarily indicative of similar response potential in a physiological sense.

Several overall conclusions appear relevant to our understanding of human conflict. The predispositional characteristics of subjects as revealed in attitude scales strongly suggests that an identified subgroup will not be sympathetic to the suffering of their fellow human beings. Thus "one plausible hypothesis emerging from both studies is that 'saturation' stimuli providing an overload of modeled behavior to be discouraged (e.g., violence) may be counterproductive if the prior disposition is favorable; rather than revulsion, the person may be more likely to orient to the stimulus and, perhaps, acquire it even more effectively" (Watts and Sumi 1979:32). It is imperative, therefore, to understand that attempts by the mass media and the educational system, for example, to develop negative social attitudes toward violence could have seriously confounding differential effects depending on the predispositional qualities of the individuals in the target audience.

Another conclusion is that future validation studies of attitude scales will have to incorporate information about emotional reactions of subjects as indexed by physiological measures. This finding is fully consistent with the observation by Schubert in Chapter 2 that zoologists have long understood that their observations of animal behavior must be coupled with neurological and endocrinological laboratory or field research in order to fully comprehend the motivational systems of their subjects.

## Crowding and International War

Expressing a disenchantment with simple stimulus-response models of human behavior, Singer and Luterbacher (1970) have asked whether there might be a "throughput dynamic" that links the stimulus of crowding with the incidence of international war in human societies. This question is based upon a rather well-developed literature in animal studies which appears to provide evidence for just such a linkage. For example, these writers (1970:4) point out that work with mice, deer, birds, woodchucks, and muskrats indicates that crowding produces internal biochemical changes similar to those that result from other forms of stress. In addition, changes in odor, inhibition of lactation, and lowered resistance to infectious diseases also appear to result from increases in population density. Moreover, Singer and Luterbacher (1970:5) point out that "rapid population buildup in rabbits, rats, and lemmings leads to such high and widespread stress levels that large-scale suicide often eventuates. Even without the suicidal pattern, the sharp increase in density leads to such levels of stress and adrenal hyperactivity that animals can no longer survive in an environment which they had earlier found quite hospitable and in which there still remained an adequate food supply."

Informed by work in animal behavior, and in an attempt to test their suspicions that crowding or high population densities contributed to the outbreak of international wars, Bremer, Singer, and Luterbacher (1973) examined the behavior of European nations during the 150-year period of 1816 to 1965. Data were collected for all intra-European state-initiated conflicts that resulted in an excess of 1000 battle deaths of military participants. Twenty-four such wars were fought during the time period under examination and resulted in 22,032,480 fatalities. The researchers also collected data on forty-nine conflicts outside the European continent that resulted in 732,400 European battle deaths.

Several issues of research design deserve mentioning. Bremer et al. (1973) were aware that a nation of high population density could be conceptualized as either predator or prey. Their research, however, focused on presumed predatory behavior, i.e., they attempted to determine whether population density provoked states to *initiate* war. They were also concerned with establishing a valid index of crowding. Accepted here were standard ratios between population and area, but also included were calculations on the changes in these density ratios over the preceding five-year period. The latter was taken into account on the assumption that rapid increases in density might contribute to social instability.

The general results of this study were similar to those produced by Welch and Booth in an intranation context: the association between crowding and aggressive behavior at the international level appears weak. Bremer et al. (1973:345) "found little relationship over time between how crowded a nation was and several measures of its war participation, [even] controlling for nation-specific differences such as culture." Further, variations in technological development over time did not correlate with conflict initiation. However, "initiators of war were generally urbanizing faster than those whom they attacked." This was explained by linking war proneness to industrialization rather than developing a connection between crowding and international war.

In spite of their inability to show a clear relationship between population densities and initiation of combat, Bremer et al. (1973:345-346) raised three questions that could at some point encourage researchers to reopen this question. Is it possible that there is a nonlinear relationship between human crowding and the outbreak of conflict? The evidence from biological researchers appears to establish clearly delineated density thresholds that when crossed, result in conflictful behavior. It is quite probable that all of the European nations that were the cases for this study fell below the critical crowding threshold. If this is found to be true, it is likely that in the future, as nations approach this threshold, we might witness an increasing incidence of conflict driven by high population densities. If nothing else, crowding could provide aggressive-minded leaders with a rationale for the initiation of conflict.

A second consideration raised by Bremer et al. relates to the appropriateness of generalizing about crowding and international conflict from an exclusively European data base. They point out that most of the densely populated nations are in Asia, and that including them in an internationally focused (i.e., not exlusively European) study might yield substantially different findings. Such a study remains to be conducted.

Third, in reflecting on the relationship between crowding and combat in animal societies, Bremer et al. (1973:346) emphasize that crowding by itself was not a sufficient cause of conflict. Rather, as indicated in the experiments of Calhoun (1962), normal social patterns of dominance and submission were disorganized, and this disorganization became an important intervening variable between crowding and combat. Projecting this to the international system, Bremer et al. (1973:346) inferred that "as the number of people and nations grows and outstrips natural and man-made resources, objective and subjective levels of relative deprivation are likely to rise sharply. As people begin to feel that the norms of distributive justice are not being satisfied, they will increasingly challenge the global pecking order and the institutions which perpetuate it." They go on to suggest that "as the animal experimenter could so rearrange access to, and distribution of, valued objects as to permit the groups to adapt to larger populations, so must those who control resources in the global system." Whether this will be possible appears to be a major question for international politics in the late twentieth century.

## Public Policy Issues Associated with Human Conflict

We have seen that conflict and aggression are closely associated with behavior in human social situations. Yet while most societies have developed reasonable though differing forms of control of internal aggression, it is in the international system that we find less effective measures of control. Indeed, an awareness of biological possibilities in social perspective has created a situation in which the life sciences might contribute inadvertently to the impetus of international war through the development of new forms of conflict. Let us look briefly at several examples.

As a result of World War I, nations became aware of the potential military usefulness of asphyxiating and poisonous gases as well as certain bacteriological substances. Though very little use was given to these agents during World War II, the Vietnam War saw the development of an awareness of possible artificial changes in the environment as a means of conducting warfare. In that conflict, herbicides and defoliants were utilized to alter the biosphere for military purposes. During that time also, decision makers and analysts realized that a significantly broader range of instruments of environmental conflict were to become available in the future. These included climatic manipulations such as the artificial production of earthquakes, seismic waves, land erosion, precipitation, cyclones, and tornadoes. It was also learned that it might be possible to interfere with the stratospheric ozone layer which would allow for an increase in the amount of ultraviolet light reaching the earth's surface. Such a development could adversely effect exposed biological systems. The ozone layer can be manipulated by either a nuclear explosion in the stratosphere or by the injection of ozone-attracting substances such as chlorine.

While the 1963 Partial Test Ban Treaty and the 1972 convention prohibiting the development, production, and stockpiling of toxic and biological weapons represent an effort to come to grips with the awesome challenges to human survival posed by new knowledge in the life sciences and technology, political observers generally have failed to appreciate these developments. Rather than the shrinkage of the arena of human conflict, we are likely to witness a vast expansion not only on this planet but also in outer space (Jasani, 1978). It is perhaps significant that in 1969 a military alliance, the North Atlantic Treaty Organization, created a committee on the Challenges of Modern Society to explore the problems of the human environment (Huntley, 1972).

At a different but related level, Stegenga (1979) has reflected on how conflict might be controlled within the individual. Frightening as this might seem, he describes four methods that focus on "internal causal factors." In animals, but only rarely in humans, brain tumors and certain parts of the brain such as the amygdala have been removed surgically and successfully to eliminate extremely violent behavior. Brain surgery of this type, of course, is irreversible. A second method involves precise and carefully controlled electrical stimulation of areas of the brain that normally inhibit violent activity. Knowledge regarding these "limbic stop points," however, appears not to be well developed at this time. On the assumption that imbalances in an individual's hormonal system might be a cause of violent behavior, female hormones such as estrogen have been administered to violent males to reduce aggression. A fourth method has emerged from the field of pharmacotherapy involving the use of a variety of drugs to treat aberrant behavior.

One of the difficulties of these internal methods of control is that they depend on the prior identification of the violent individual. In a physiological sense, such identification is often difficult, though some disorders such as hypoglycemia and temporal lobe epilepsy are easily diagnosed (Stegenga, 1979:8). As a group, all four of these methods represent means for manipulating the internal environment of an individual human being. While much of the technical knowledge to do this is now available, more is sure to be generated in the future. Stegenga (1978:8, 13) hastens to point out that a model of the control of aggression based only on physiological variables is inaccurate. Social variables such as psychological counseling, job training, or incarceration must continue to play a contributing role. Indeed, we are presently moving toward a more accurate and more human understanding of violent behavior that includes social, psychological, and physiological considerations.

In examining the biological dimensions of human aggression we cannot help being struck by the apparently great potential for abuse and the challenges to conventional morality. Safeguards are clearly needed. As Stegenga observes (1979:13), "the participants in the current spirited debate are agreed on this need and differ only about who should draw the lines that must be drawn and where exactly they should be drawn." These are questions of public policy that must be answered shortly, probably by political scientists working with the concerned natural scientists and governmental leaders.

But at a more specific level, will our knowledge of the biological dimensions of aggression lead us to any policy related observations regarding the future of war? We can agree with Stegenga that Clark's (1971) suggestion to employ psychopharmacological means, i.e., the administration of a "peace pill," to control the aggressive proclivities of national leaders is naive. However, further down the chain of command, as Stegenga suggests, are lesser ranking individuals who, because of the critical positions, might easily be required to ingest drugs to control aggressive impulses. If U.S. military personnel who serve on Polaris submarines can be tested periodically to determine their psychological health, as indeed they are, it does not seem too unreasonable to speculate that a physical examination revealing an aggression-related internal physiological disturbance might result in some form of control therapy. While justifications for the type of screening are easy to construct for critical positions within the armed forces, "the weakest link might continue to be at the top of the chain of command" where submission to screening will be impossible to achieve (Stegenga, 1979:15). On the other hand, there seems to be little to be gained by discussing the physiological or social control of the aggressive tendencies in high ranking political elites until we have determined a precise set of examination rules to be applied to the leaders of all or most of the national units in existence today. Such a development is unlikely to take place.

## Conclusions

We have looked at several dimensions of interests that political scientists have had in the biopolitics of human conflict. Those interests have been uneven and inconsistent; many gaps exist in our basic understanding of conflict. But because a knowledge of conflict is so central to our conceptions of political behavior, it seems reasonable to expect that political scientists will be more sensitive to examining perspectives from other disciplines, especially physiology. Such an outlook might yield fruitful interdisciplinary studies that could offer much more accurate appraisals of the nature of human political conflict.

## References

Beitz, C. P. and T. Hermann, eds. (1973) *Peace and War*. San Francisco: W. H. Freeman.

Bremer, S., J. D. Singer, and U. Luterbacher. (1973) "The Population Density and War Proneness of European Nationals, 1816-1965." *Comparative Political Studies*, 6, 3, October:329-348.

Calhoun, J. B. (1962) "Population Density and Social Pathology." *Scientific American* 206, February:139-146.

Christie, R. and F. L. Geis, (1970) *Studies in Machiavellianism*. New York: Academic Press.

Clark, K. B. (1971) "The Pathos of Power: A Psychological Perspective." *American Psychologist*: 1047-1057.

Colton, T. (1969) "The 'New Biology' and the Causes of War." *Canadian Journal of Political Science*, December:434-447.

Coser, L. (1956) *The Functions of Social Conflict*. New York: Free Press.

Corning, P. A. (1975) "An Evolutionary Paradigm for the Study of Human Aggression," in M. A. Nettleship, R. D. Givens, and A. Nettleship, eds.

————. (1973) "Human Violence: Some Causes and Implications," in C. P. Beitz and T. Herman, eds.

Corning, P. A., and C. H. Corning. (1972) "Toward a General Theory of Violent Aggression." *Social Science Information* 11, June-August:7-35.

Davies, J. C. (1970) "Violence and Aggression: Innate or Not?" *West-*

*ern Political Quarterly* 23, September:611-623.

Dougherty, J. E. and R. L. Pfaltzgraff, Jr. (1971) *Contending Theories of International Relations.* Philadelphia: Lippincott.

Hare, R. D. (1973) "Orienting and Defensive Responses to Visual Stimuli." *Psychophysiology* 10:453-464.

Huntley, J. R. (1972) *Man's Environment and the Atlantic Alliance.* Brussels: NATO Information Service.

Jasani, B. M. (1978) *Outer Space—Battlefield of the Future?* New York: Crane, Russak.

Lacey, J. I. and B. C. Lacey. (1974) "On Heart Rate Responses and Behavior: A Reply to Elliot." *Journal of Personality and Social Psychology* 30:1-18.

————. (1970) "Some Autonomic Central Nervous System Interrelationships," in P. Black, ed., *Physiological Correlates of Emotion.* New York: Academic Press.

Levine, S. and N. Scotch. (1970) "Perspectives on Stress Research," in S. Levine and N. Scotch, eds., *Social Stress.* Chicago: Aldine.

McNeil, E. B., ed. (1965) *The Nature of Human Conflict.* Englewood Cliffs, N.J.: Prentice-Hall.

Moyer, K. E. (1971) *The Physiology of Hostility.* Chicago: Markham.

Nettleship, M. A., R. D. Givens, and A. Nettleship. (1975) *War, Its Causes and Correlates.* The Hague: Mouton.

Pettman, R. (1975) *Human Behavior and World Politics.* New York: St. Martin's Press.

Phillips, C. (n.d.) "Evolution: Biological *and* Cultural." Unpublished manuscript.

Ridgway, M. B. (1956) *Soldier.* New York: Harper & Brothers.

Singer, J. D. and U. Luterbacher. (1970) "Crowding and Combat in Animal and Human Societies: The European State System, 1816-1965," Paper presented to the Eighth Congress of the International Political Science Association, Munich, August.

Stegenga, J. A. (1979) "The Physiology of Aggression." Paper presented to the annual convention of the International Studies Association, Toronto, March.

————. (1972) "Personal Aggressiveness and War." *International Journal of Tensions* 2, 4:22-36.

Wallace, A. F. C. (1956) "Revitalization Movements." *American Anthropologist* 58, 2:264-281.

Watts, M. W. (1977) "Psychophysiological Analysis of Personality/Attitude Scales: Some Theoretical Rationale and Experimental Results." Paper presented to the William Munro Seminar on Biobehavioral Political Science, Stanford University, April.

––––––. (1976) "Stress and Physiological Aspects of Political Behavior: The Psychophysiological Component of Aggressive Attitudes." Paper presented to the Tenth Congress of the International and Political Science Association, Edinburgh, August.

Watts, M. W. and D. Sumi. (1979) "Studies in the Physiological Component of Aggression-Related Social Attitudes." *American Journal of Political Science* (forthcoming).

––––––. (1976) "Attitudes and Physiological Response to Audiovisual Display of Aggressive Social Behavior." Paper presented to the annual convention of the Midwest Political Science Association, Chicago, April-May.

# 7

# The Future of Biopolitics

A major thesis of this book has been that political beings are not ethereal essences floating around in an intellectual construct called a political system. Because human nature is rational, psychological, *and* physical, analysts of political behavior must begin to conceive of the subjects of their investigations as biological beings with intellective capacities. At the present state in the development of the discipline, we can characterize ourselves as having ignored an enormous amount of information about humanity and its real nature, that is its nature *as it is lived.* Because our vision has often been narrowly focused down safe, well-traveled tunnels, we have been insufficiently attentive to the powerful findings of the twentieth-century life sciences. Indeed, we may have been guilty of the arbitrary exclusion that was alluded to in the introductory chapter.

When the potential exists to enhance explanations of political phenomena with variables from the life sciences, we should not fail to realize that potential. When we find evidence that human political behavior is shaped or influenced by biological considerations, we cannot, in the spirit of intellectual honesty, ignore that information. Thus, it is incumbent upon us to add a biological perspective to our work; in doing so we need not engage in a blind acceptance of a biological determinism that pays no heed to human purposive activities.

We must adopt a more comprehensive definition of human nature, one that includes in an operational way the biological as well as the rational and psychological. If we do so, we will have to pay the price of making our discipline increasingly more complex. At the same time, however, the findings generated will be more realistic and—we hope—more accurate. Such a broadened definition of human nature will force us to adopt a much more basic orientation in our research efforts.

## Strategies for Pursuing a Biopolitics of Human Life

As we have seen, researchers who have worked in the area now known as biopolitics have been interested in several aspects of the life sciences. The most prominent among these are ethology, evolutionary studies including population biology, and what might very loosely be referred to as physiology.

All of these areas will have an increasing relevance to political inquiry. Ethology has given us many useful organizing concepts including territoriality, bonding, imprinting, dominance, and ritualized behavior. Ethology has the powerful advantage that many of its insights have grown out of a comparative perspective on animal social behavior. Some work is beginning to link data from animals with human data, leading to the emerging field of human ethology (see Eibl-Eibesfeldt, 1970).

Population biology has proved to be a rich source of information on evolution, and at least one political scientist (Peter Corning) has focused almost exclusively on the evolutionary perspective in his work. Animal studies have also contributed a good deal of knowledge in this area.

Physiologically oriented work has adopted perspectives from subspecialties that have focused, for example, on nutrition, health, neurology, psychophysiology, and medicine. This research is different from that of ethology and evolution in that is has concentrated, for the most part, on the individual human being or on specific groups of humans rather than on the species as a whole.

Yet several problems remain with these orientations. For example, the body of ethological literature poses some methodological and epistemological difficulties when an attempt is made to extend it to human behavior. Peterson (1977), a political scientist, has strongly cautioned his colleagues on what he calls the "hazards of cross-species comparison," particularly in extending primate investigations to the study of human behavior. Comparisons have followed a fairly typical methodological approach that, according to Peterson (1977:3), consists of the following schedule of tasks: "(1) a search of the primate literature to detect patterns which may have human political analogues; (2) pointing out human behavior which seems similar to the primate pattern(s); and (3) the consequent positing of common biological explanations for this similarity (e.g., similarity because of congruent selection pressure or descent from the same ancestor)." (See also Sahlins, 1976.)

What is the nature of a criterion for similarity? At what point can we say that dissimilarity exists? If we are examining human political analogues, precise definitions of "humanness" usually are not offered. Furthermore, there are numerous cultural differences among human beings that influence behavior patterns.

Because human beings have the capacity for symbolic communication of a very high order, it can be argued that Homo sapiens is a fundamentally different creature from those found in the animal world. Indeed, speech transmits not only information but also meaning, and this implies that human culture is strongly conditioned by communication. Such culture might not be as genetically influenced as that of, say, non-human primates.

While other examples of difficulties in moving across species lines can be offered, the several cited above should suffice to make the point that a political scientist, whose interests focus on the human being, will necessarily embroil himself in arguments relating to the validity of cross-species comparisons by adopting a rigorously ethological perspective. Not only have some American scientists recently brought a lawsuit against popularizers of ethological knowledge, but scientists in the United Kingdom have formed the British Society for Social

Responsibility in Science with a working group on sociobiology to examine distortions of ethological work as they have been applied to human behavior.[1] These problems, however, should not deter imaginative political scientists from a careful use of ethological information in their research work.

Perhaps the most productive avenues for the political scientist to exploit in developing a more operationally comprehensive definition of human nature lie in the life sciences that are devoted exclusively to the study of man. The bodies of knowledge that have dealt with the human organism directly and empirically include medicine, psychopharmacology, neuroanatomy, biochemistry, epidemiology, human biology, psychosomatic medicine, psychophysiology, human physiology, human endocrinology and behavioral ecology. Each of these is a significant discipline in its own right; each has focused on the human species; each has the potentiality of adding to our understanding of political society. Much of the work relating to the study of elites, conflict and aggression, and even the general political system, has grown out of these life sciences. However, it is this empirically useful knowledge that is the most difficult to acquire for a political scientist. One important reason why progress linking the "harder" life sciences with political science has been slow is that political scientists who want to utilize these disciplines must undertake serious retraining in the form of heavy immersion in the literature of another field and, if possible, the establishment of a mentor relationship with a colleague in the appropriate life science discipline. Such arrangements often are satisfactory for establishing credentials to *begin* interdisciplinary work. However, as work develops, the substantive and methodological issues associated with further progress become increasingly complex. However, there is one development that most assuredly should not take place.

When interdisciplinary work becomes complex, there is a danger that biologically oriented political researchers may "give up" because the knowledge required is highly technical and progress is slow. This could result in a situation in which the nontechnical literature of the life sciences—since it is the literature that we can read with comfort—becomes the only biological information relevant to our inquiries. This would be unfortunate because it would create a situation in which biopolitics would remain in the realm of speculative thought. That is not to say that such thought does not have an important contribution to make to the study of biopolitics; but without a heavy emphasis on the empirical findings of the life sciences, biopolitics will be little more than a "literary" area devoid of any basic knowledge about real political behavior.

In sum, the danger with the ethological thrust is that researchers might treat Homo sapiens as little more than another animal species; the danger with what we have called the "physiological" thrust is that work might become overly complicated and "payoffs" so distant that researchers will decline the challenge. Fortunately, biopolitical scholars have shown a remarkable awareness of these potential problems and it is unlikely that either will come to pass.

## Some Elementary Needs

Several important future requirements are necessary for biopolitics to establish itself firmly as an innovative orientation in the discipline. First, we need a healthier and more optimistic orientation to *basic* research. There are two implications of this need. While the "so what?" question should be asked of all scholarship at all times, this question should be one of the honest inquiry and anticipation, not disdain. Scholars using human biological variables in their work are finding significant associations between those variables and political behavior. And that is really quite enough at this point in our attempts to utilize a more comprehensive definition of political humanity. To require that all research have immediately identifiable applications to the political system or to public policy is to effectively close off the development of basic research questions and studies. Applications are not always readily apparent in basic research work, as we all know, but an expanded knowledge of associations—citing the natural sciences again as an example—will ultimately lead to causal inference and to practical applications.

An additional implication of the development of a more healthy attitude toward basic research is that we must, as Wahlke (1976:258) has suggested, employ experimental methods in our work. Experimental orientations must guide our inquiries in both laboratory and real-world environments. Indeed, we might quite intentionally design studies that would incorporate both settings. An experimental orientation may lead us into new research methods that many will initially find awkward. But we should not be fearful of the unfamiliar nor should we shrink from reporting negative results. It will be important for journals to publish negative as well as positive findings and our attitudes toward all reports will need to be positive and open.

The new approach to basic research will also lead quite naturally to the need for a more comprehensive knowledge of biopolitical research methods. Until such methods are further developed, collated in texts, and widely known, it will be difficult to intensify our work in the years ahead. The methodology of ethological research could exercise a profound influence on a broad spectrum of political questions. So too, the methodology of physiology, especially psychophysiology, should provide new dimensions in the methodological training of professional political scientists.

A third need concerns the necessity of developing interdisciplinary teams of researchers. Properly constructed, these teams can overcome many of the problems that result when individuals attempt to blend knowledge from another discipline into their own disciplinary stores of information. However, meaningful interdisciplinary cooperation, normally praised in the abstract, is not easy to develop. Joint studies must be conceived in ways that are professionally productive to each discipline represented in the effort if they are to expand the limits of methodological tools, approaches, and substantive insights available to the single scholar. Because of the complexities involved, this kind of collaboration is frequently difficult to arrange on a long-term basis. One effective way to address this problem would be to encourage academic departments to offer regular appointments to relevant professionals from outside their own disciplines. But the likelihood of such a development taking place on any meaningful scale is negligible.

Given this situation, a fourth need becomes obvious. If biopolitics is to establish itself as a continuing orientation within the discipline of political science, interdisciplinary curricula for the training of new scholars will have to be created (see Caldwell, 1979, Corning, 1978; and Kort and Maxson, 1978). But as we have seen in this book, biopolitics is more than an "orientation"; rather, biopolitics speaks to a fundamental reordering of the substantive knowledge needed to understand political life. Such a reordering is required across all the subfields of the discipline. Somit (1968) saw this situation clearly over a decade ago when he suggested that political scientists acquire at least a minimum of biological expertise to allow them to utilize the literature of the life sciences.

Further, we are not dealing here with a momentary aberration or a fad that will wither away in due time. The twentieth-century impact of the life sciences on the understanding of social behavior across all species has been awesome. The effects of these are being felt in sociology, economics, history, and psychology. In short, the necessity to incorporate biological considerations into our understanding of social man will not disappear. It is imperative that at least a few political science departments launch pilot programs to train students to work at the disciplinary juncture of the life and social sciences.

Fifth, and related to curricular considerations, is the need for some students of biopolitics to become interested in the political policy relevance of certain aspects of the life sciences. In the foregoing chapters we have discussed numerous public policy dimensions of biopolitical research. Only a few scholars have been interested in pursuing such an orientation, most notably in technology and genetic engineering. However, the "applications" side of biopolitics should expand in the immediate future because of its strong vocational prospects. But a word of caution is in order. Given the preliminary state of much of our work in biopolitics, we cannot afford to lessen our basic research efforts. Because interdisciplinary progress is often slow, a much more intensive devotion to basic research is not only desirable but also the sine qua non of a meaningful expansion of biopolitical knowledge.

The willingness to make a long-term intellectual commitment toward pursuing a research question of biopolitical interest is a sixth important need. Because progress in the uncharted areas of any discipline is frequently difficult, researchers could easily become discouraged. Wise colleagues can offer support and encouragement, especially to their junior partners, over the course of a long-term research effort. Demands for immediate and numerous publications should not be allowed to distort the inquiry process.

Seventh, we need to rid ourselves of the fear of taking intellectual risks. By and large, political science has been a conservative discipline. However, scholarly tradition is built, not just guarded and maintained. At the intersection of the social and biological sciences can be found many enticing research questions holding the prospect of producing stunning insights and knowledge that could enhance and expand traditional wisdom. But to address these questions requires rather high risk research efforts; that is, after a significant investment of time the findings might be negative. If we are going to make intellectual breakthroughs, however, we are going to have to take these risks. I am confident that it will be worth the investment and that substantial intellectual payoffs will result.

As an interim measure, those who aspire to pursue a biopolitical orientation can become familiar with natural science journals that deal with behavioral aspects of human nature. Several of these journals are:

> *Journal of Human Stress*
> *Journal of Psychosomatic Medicine*
> *Journal of Health and Social Behavior*
> *Journal of Social Biology*
> *Journal of Medical Psychology*
> *Journal of Applied Physiology*
> *Journal of Medical Ethics*

*Journal of Biological Psychology*
*Biology and Human Affairs*
*Developmental Psychobiology*
*Environmental Biology & Medicine*
*Journal of Social and Biological Structures*
*Physiology and Behavior*
*Journal of Medicine and Philosophy*
*Psychophysiology*
*Behavioral Neuropsychiatry*
*International Journal of Social Psychiatry*
*Neuroscience and Behavioral Physiology*
*Human Ecology*
*Journal of Environmental Health*
*Urban Ecology*
*Bioethics Digest*
*Environmental Health*
*Culture, Medicine and Psychiatry*
*The Behavioral and Brain Sciences*
*Brain and Language*
*Medical Anthropology*
*Behavioral Engineering*
*Environment and Behavior*
*Journal of Genetic Psychology*
*Journal of Biosocial Science*
*Journal of Ecology*
*Ecological Studies*
*Behaviorial Ecology and Sociobiology*
*Biobehavioral Reviews*
*International Journal of Psychobiology*
*Progress in Psychobiology and Physiological Psychology*
*Ethology and Sociobiology*

Another publication that has grown out of the humanities and often deals with natural science topics is the *Journal of Interdisciplinary History*. This partial listing of journals is offered as evidence that scholars in the human life sciences *are now generating and will continue to generate* a good deal of behaviorally oriented information about the human species. We cannot afford to ignore this work.

Finally, it will be important for us to develop professional affiliations with appropriate organizations of colleagues in related fields such as human ethology, animal behavior, primatology, psychophysiology, and social ecology.

## Conclusions

In our efforts to develop a more human operational definition of Homo sapiens, we should always remember that we are political scientists whose inquiries should begin with a professional desire to understand *political* problems, issues, and behaviors. After identifying the subject area of our research, we should ask ourselves how the human life sciences might contribute to a more complete understanding of the political phenomena under investigation. In those instances where the life sciences contribute nothing, we should not bend to employ them. Moreover, we should be cautious about encouraging a biological reductionism that leaves little room for rational judgments and the mediating effects of social situations.

As research progresses in the vein suggested by this book, we probably should resist the temptation to build grand theory. Our most productive work will, in all likelihood, be in developing islands of biopolitical knowledge from which general theory will emerge at a later time. Once we feel comfortable with the inclusion of biological variables in our work, the real "post-behavioral revolution" will have been accomplished. At that point a much more basic research-oriented political science will have been established. At that point too, the "Great Academic Wall" separating the disciplines that concerned Glendon Schubert (1976) should be in the process of breaking down. Perhaps by that time we will have developed curricular programs based upon a more comprehensive definition of human nature that will train students to carry out biopolitically based research with ease.

Some critics have implied that political researchers who incorporate human biological variables into their work in an attempt to understand political phenomena and behaviors are somehow guilty of adopting an antihumanist posture toward political life. This book has argued that our discipline has functioned, for the most part, with an incomplete operational definition of human nature. To the extent that our views of humanity have been distorted we have been antihumanist for we have failed to appreciate the true complexity of human nature. Likewise, to the extent that we blend human biological variables into what we already know about human rational behavior, we will become increasingly humanistic. And that seems to me to be a worthy objective.

It is no longer a question of *whether* we should incorporate human life science data into our studies of human social behavior: that is already being done by the life scientists, and the journals listed above ought to be a minimal testament to this activity. The more crucial questions are: who is best equipped to study human social behavior, the life scientist or the social scientist, and who will have a deeper appreciation of humanistic values, the life scientist or the social scientist?

**Note**

1. For news stories on these developments see *New Scientist*, December 15, 1977, p. 711, and January 5, 1978, p. 30.

**References**

Caldwell, L. K. (1979) "Implications of Biopolitics: Reflections on a Politics of Survival." Paper presented to the annual convention of the International Society for Political Psychology, Washington, D.C., May.

Corning, P. A. (1978) "Biopolitics: Toward a New Political Science." Paper presented to the annual convention of the American Political Science Association, New York, August 31–September 3.

Eibl-Eibesfeldt, I. (1970) *Ethology: The Biology of Behavior*. New York: Holt, Rinehart and Winston.

Kort, F. and S. C. Maxson. (1978) "The Study of Politics in a Biobehavioral Perspective: A Report on a Course Based on a New

Paradigm." Paper presented to the annual meeting of the American Society of Criminology, Dallas, November.

Peterson, S. A. (1977) "On the Hazards of Cross-Species Comparison: Primates and Human Politics." Paper presented to the Research and Planning Committee for Biology and Politics of the International Political Science Association, Bellagio, Italy, November.

Sahlins, M. (1976) *The Use and Abuse of Biology*. Ann Arbor: University of Michigan Press.

Schubert, G. (1976) "Politics as a Life Science: How and Why the Impact of Modern Biology Will Revolutionize the Study of Political Behavior," in A. Somit, ed., *Biology and Politics*. The Hague: Mouton.

Somit, A. (1968) "Toward a More Biologically-Oriented Political Science: Ethology and Psychopharmacology." *Midwest Journal of Political Science* 12:550-567.

Wahlke, J. (1976) "Observations on Biopolitical Study," in A. Somit, ed., *Biology and Politics*. The Hague: Mouton.

# Index